The Evolution of Terrestrial and Extraterrestrial Life

Where in the World is God?

The Evolution of Terrestrial and Extraterrestrial Life

Where in the World is God?

Proceedings of the Seventh Annual
Goshen Conference on Religion and Science

Ted Peters
Professor of Systematic Theology
at Pacific Lutheran Theological Seminary and
the Graduate Theological Union, Berkeley

Edited by: Carl S. Helrich
Goshen College

Published by Pandora Press

The Goshen Conference on Religion and Science

The Goshen Conference on Religion and Science, a yearly lecture series, features distinguished scholars. The proceedings are edited by Carl S. Helrich and published by Pandora Press.

Religion and Science: God, Evolution and the Soul
Nancy Murphy (2001)

A Universe of Ethics Morality and Hope
George F.R. Ellis (2002)

The Dialogue between Science and Religion
Antje Jackelén (2003)

Purpose, Evolution and the Mystery of Life
John F. Haught (2004)

Cosmology, Evolution, and Resurrection Hope
Robert John Russell (2005)

Religion-and-Science as Spiritual Quest for Meaning
Philip Hefner (2006)

The Evolution of Terrestrial and Extraterrestrial Life
Ted Peters (2007)

Dedication

I dedicate this book to Lydia Magdalen Frase, Nina Elise Frase, Jacqueline Nicole Carter, Jessica Loryn Carter, Kayla Christine Carter, Madeline Lulu Peters, and David William Peters, each of whom make a grandfather very joyful.

Library and Archives Canada Cataloguing in Publication

Peters, Ted, 1941-

The evolution of terrestrial and extraterrestrial life : where in the world is God? : proceedings of the Seventh Annual Goshen Conference on Religion and Science / Ted Peters ; edited by Carl S. Helrich.

Conference held in Goshen, Indiana, Mar. 16-17, 2007.
Includes bibliographical references and index.
ISBN 978-1-894710-85-5

1. Religion and science--Congresses. I. Helrich, Carl S. II. Goshen Conference on Religion and Science (7th : 2007 : Goshen, Ind.) III. Title.

BT103.P47 2008 261.5'5 C2008-902938-0

33 Kent Avenue
Kitchener, Ontario N2G 3R2

Cover photograph: Untitled from *The Twelfth Station*
© Karl Griffiths-Fulton 2008

Acknowledgements

These lectures are revisions of those delivered at the 7th Annual Goshen Conference on Religion and Science, Goshen College, March 16-19, 2007.

A variant of lecture one, "Christian God Talk While Listening to Atheists, Pluralists, and Muslims," was published as an article in *Dialog, A Journal of Theology* 46:2 (Summer 2007) 84-103.

An abbreviated variant of lecture two, "Evolution, Evil, and the Theology of the Cross," was delivered as a lecture at Lund University in Sweden on May 30, 2007. It will appear in the journal, *Svensk Teologisk Kvartalskrift.*

A summary of lecture three, "Extraterrestrial Life and Exotheology," was presented to the University of Arizona, Steward Observatory, as part of the "Astrobiology and the Sacred" lecture series, February 28, 2007.

Contents

Editor's Preface

The basic question Ted Peters posed for the 2007 Goshen Conference on Religion and Science was: Where in the world is God? In three lectures he uncovered aspects of that question and revealed some of the difficulties we encounter in answering that question. The simplicity of the claim that God is everywhere becomes mired when we turn to the realities of our life experiences on this planet. The difficulty becomes deeper if we consider our biological history. And our answer to the question must also embrace what we have learned and are learning about the universe. In the Twenty-First Century, we have reason to speculate that the universe includes many centers of life beyond our planet. How do we understand the second person of the Trinity and the role of Jesus the Christ in the salvation of all of creation? Our conviction that God is everywhere, and embraces all of creation with a salvific love, must include all that is.

The Mennonite theologian, with Amish roots, Alvin J. Beachy, once said that difficult questions, by definition, do not have simple answers. And Ted Peters provided no simple answers to the question of where in the world God is. We must consider the reality of revelation in the Abrahamic religions. And then we must seriously try to understand the issues that separate us. Modern studies of animals most closely related to us genetically have revealed origins of our sinful nature. Salvation, in any understanding, must encounter the reality of a world which has an evolutionary history. How do we reconcile the brutality of predation and the brutality of human history with a loving God?

Ted Peters points to God as the source of salvation and to a Theology of the Cross as the source of our understanding. The question of the meaning of salvation is difficult and the answer to which Ted Peters points is not simple. To understand God, says Martin Luther, we must look at the cross and recognize that we do not understand God.

The discussions, which are part of these proceedings, are a record of the way in which conference participants engaged the aspects of the question Ted Peters presented. Participants included undergraduate and graduate students, professional people, theologians, and scientists. The issues raised, and the responses provide insight into the question facing the conference and into Ted Peters' thinking. There are no simple answers. But we can gain a deeper understanding of the question. And this question is central to our very being.

These proceedings include the homily delivered in the worship service that is a part of the conference. The homily was delivered in 2007 by Joseph A. Bracken, S.J., a philosopher from Xavier University in Cincinnati, Ohio. The title of the homily was Remarks on the Relationship between Religion and Science.

I want to personally thank David Powell for his careful transcribing of the recordings from the conference.

Carl Helrich
Goshen
January 4, 2008

Lecture One

Finding God in the Niche of Atheism, Pluralism, and Islam

Christians believe in one God who is Father, Son, and Holy Spirit. This Trinitarian God is the ground and source of all reality, all life, all meaning; and in the grace of this God we live and move and have our being. Yet, this Christian belief finds itself in a life-and-death struggle. In the struggle for the survival of the fittest religious vision, it is not clear which will emerge the winner.

Suppose we liken the Christian understanding of God to a competitor for an evolutionary niche. We Christians want our symbols of a loving and gracious God to become selected for by hearts and minds. Like a juicy species of fruit, we want as many as possible to enjoy faith's good taste and be nourished by what they imbibe. However, other life forms want to be selected for the very same environment. One of these will likely win if the Christian vision goes extinct.

The three religious life forms now competing for the Christian niche are atheism, pluralism, and Islam. The current environment of evolutionary adaptedness or EEA, to offer an extended metaphor, finds these three movements competing to become the one that survives.

Like fire ants swarming, the first is a new breed of *Evangelical Atheists* which has swept into the religious niche. Atheism is no longer the effete doctrine of a worn out naturalism. Recent legal defeats meted out to creationism and Intelligent Design, plus a growing worldwide disdain for fundamentalism in all its forms, have emboldened the atheists. Marching to the tune of a re-tooled Darwinism, they are aiming at the total extinction of what they deem irrational religion.

Secondly, like another species of religious fruit, *Islam* is vying for the same niche Christians seek. Muslims have since the days of the Qur'an insisted that the prime reality is God; and there is but one God and but one religion through which God can be properly worshipped and obeyed. The enemies of Islam's God are not only the atheists, but also the polytheists. Among the polytheists, Muslim's list their religious kin, apostate Jews and

Trinitarian Christians. Secularized Jews have lost their loyalty to the one God, substituting their peoplehood for faith in God. But, the Christians are even more culpable of blasphemy, because of the tri-theism inherent in the doctrine of the Trinity.

Thirdly, like worms burrowing into ripening fruit and devouring it from within, *religious pluralists* are competing for the niche previously occupied by the Western monotheisms: Judaism, Christianity, and Islam. The pluralists have no tolerance for intolerance. They see intolerance daily in religious absolutism, in narrow-mindedness, in lack of understanding and lack of charity toward believers belonging to alternative religious traditions. Pluralists want to combat religious imperialism with a doctrine of religious equality or parity so as to bring intercultural peace. Such equality can be affirmed if all will affirm the equal validity of the diverse ways in which God is experienced and worshipped and obeyed.

Pluralists respect every religion. Muslims respect their own religion. Atheists respect no religion. Which position is the one most fit to survive?

In the cultural competition for the religious niche, the pluralists would like to burrow within traditional Christianity and make this one religion fight for religious diversity. Pluralists want to rid us of religious competition so that all can survive. The atheists would like to render Christianity extinct, as well as every other religion which believes in a personal God. What the new breed of evangelical atheists wants is to see science alone survive while all the world's religions disappear into our fossil history. Islam, like a competing religious species, is content to co-habit the same niche until such time as selection for survival renders Islam more fit. To survive, Islam needs to outlive Christianity, modern science, and the modern culture to which these latter two have adapted.

What is a Christian to do amidst this competition for survival? The way forward is complicated. Intellectually honest Christians appreciate and even love the pursuit of scientific knowledge; so it is particularly unnerving to see atheists claiming scientific turf as their own. The pluralists appear to be morally motivated to treat people of diverse beliefs with equal rights; and this is consistent with Christian charity. Christians see Islam as a sibling of sorts within the Abrahamic family of believers: both affirm the oneness of God even if they differ over the Trinity. Christians are inclined to adapt at least in part to science, pluralism, and Islam. Yet, Christians also have something distinct to say about God. How should Christian theologians plant fruit that will blossom and nourish?

Of the three contemporary competitors for the traditional religious niche, the most threatening to Christianity is atheism. If the new evangelical atheists turn out to be right—that scientific knowledge of the natural world is the only genuine knowledge and this leaves no room for a personal God—then they will be able to plant science where religion once grew.

The question which orients this conference is this: where in the world is God? Here in the first lecture we ask: where in the evolving world is God? In what follows, I would like to map the environment of evolutionary adaptedness—that is, the current religious niche. I would like to identify the positions taken by the atheists, the pluralists, and the Muslims. Then, from within this niche, I would like to assess the threats to a Christian who would like to stand up for certain commitments about God. Of those commitments, the single most important one is the Christian belief that God is gracious. The God who created the world we live in, and who promises to redeem it from all imperfections, is gracious in character. Even more important to the Christian theologian than establishing that God exists is to affirm that the one God is a God of grace and love.

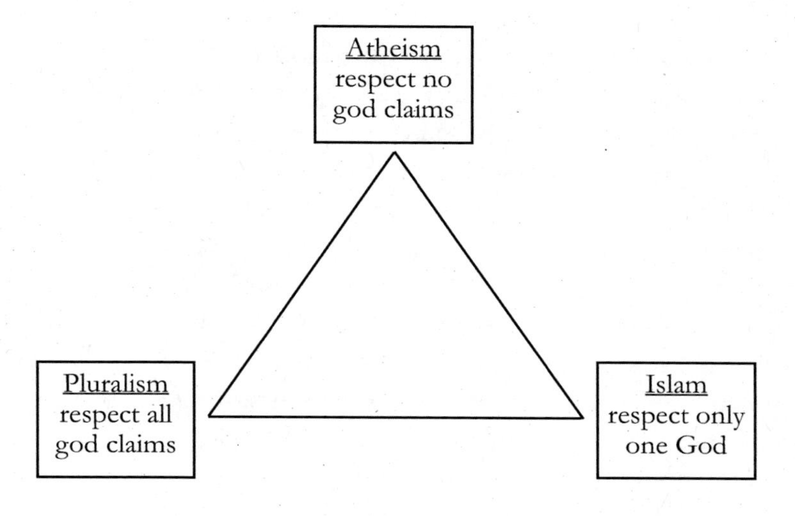

The New Breed of Aggressive Atheists

"The New Atheists...condemn not just belief in God but respect for belief in God," writes a columnist for *Wired* magazine. "Religion is not only wrong, it's evil." Religion is irrational; and it makes societies prone to violence. Religion, especially fundamentalist religion, incites violence. What today's atheists want are more converts so they can bring peace. "A band of intellectual brothers is mounting a crusade against belief in God."[1] Curiously, the new atheists are evangelizing for non-belief.

If atheists would simply gather together quietly for non-worship, they would be harmless to others. If they would limit their claims to one—to the claim that no God exists—then pluralists could consider the atheist belief system just one among many, perhaps even respectable. However, the new breed of atheists is absolutist, fundamentalist, extremist, and evangelical in its approach to non-religion. Within the cultural niche traditionally occupied by religion, the new atheists want to place science. Not just any old form of atheism will do. It is a scientized atheism that is seeking to replace religion.

The new atheists are pretenders to the throne of natural science. They have staked out a claim that natural science is their kingdom. They are putting up no-trespassing signs to keep religious believers out. "Atheism, and its justification through science, is the apotheosis of the Enlightenment," writes Oxford chemistry professor, Peter Atkins.[2] Stanford's Van Harvey observes that "a great deal of modern atheism...rests on the conviction that theism of any sort is incompatible with modern science."[3]

The problem with this is that science is the common possession of Christians, Jews, Muslims, and non-theists the world over. Science is not the private property of the atheists. Science does not require an exclusively materialist worldview. Nor does it require the denial of God. Yet, atheists claim science as an ally in their crusade.

Philosopher Paul Kurtz, who describes himself as a "skeptical atheist" trying to resist the "transcendental temptation," gives eloquent testimony to his belief in non-belief. God, he says, "is a figment of human imagination and contrivance, expressed creatively in religion, art, morality, and poetry. God does not exist. He is not a separate person or a being, an all-powerful, all-knowing, benevolent creator of the universe. These are all anthropocentric misattributions. To worship such a being is mistaken."[4] More than merely mistaken; to worship God is to indulge in a childish irrationality that we need to outgrow.[5]

Perhaps the most voracious among the anti-religious fire ants is Richard Dawkins.[6] Dawkins is the Oxford professor of science education who gave us the concept of the "selfish gene," and who is known for championing the field of sociobiology.[7] What is so valuable to the theologian about Dawkins is that he confronts the question of God head on. Does God exist? No. Well, probably, no. The question of God is a scientific question, he avers; and scientists can only speak in probabilities, not absolutes. So, it is Dawkins' considered scientific judgment that, most probably, God does not exist.

Now, we might ask: just what kind of God does Dawkins repudiate the existence of? After all, quite a diversity of ideas of God abounds among the world's religions, and even within single religious traditions. So, just which idea of God is Dawkins combating?

Dawkins, thankfully, is quite clear. He says he is not attacking any specific divine figure such as Yahweh, Jesus, Allah, Baal, Zeus, or Wotan. Rather, he is attacking all of them at once. All belief in such divinities can be swept up into a single "God Hypothesis," which Dawkins attempts to falsify. "I shall define the God Hypothesis more defensibly: *there exists a super-human, supernatural intelligence who deliberately designed and created the universe and everything in it, including us.*" Dawkins advocates "an alternative view: *any creative intelligence, of sufficient complexity to design anything, comes into existence only as the end product of an extended process of gradual evolution.*"[8] Let us be careful with the logic here. If God would exist, it would take the form of an eschatological existence, not a primordial existence. "If (which I don't believe for a moment) our universe was designed, and *a fortiori* if the designer reads our thoughts and hands out omniscient advice, forgiveness and redemption, the designer himself must be the end product of some kind of cumulative escalator or crane, perhaps a version of Darwinism in another universe."[9]

Even with this slim opening toward the coming into existence of a future intelligence, Dawkins closes the door on divinity. No God existed at the beginning, at the origin of the universe or at the origin of life; and no God now guides the evolutionary process of speciation. Natural selection does. Wondrously, natural selection has produced an intelligent designer, us. We *homo sapiens* are the most intelligent beings in nature's earthly history to date; and we might expect even higher intelligence to develop in the future. The evolutionary development of the human race is what Dawkins believes in; and, he contends, belief in evolution requires disbelief in God. Note how Dawkins has substituted natural selection for divine providence, and substituted the revelatory power of Darwin's theory of evolution for scripture.[10]

The kind of God Dawkins rejects is the kind of God who provides an explanation for a scientific description of the natural world. Is this what the God of Christian believers is supposed to do? Not exactly. Take the thought of George Coyne, for instance. Dr. Coyne is an astronomer and a Roman Catholic priest who for many years directed astrophysical research at the Vatican Observatory. Coyne cautions people of faith against trying to turn God into an explanation. He notes that the phrase, "mind of God," is used by scientists to describe the full set of nature's laws, even the will-o-the-wisp Unified Field Theory. Yet, this is not literally God. "Even if we discover the Mind of God, we will not have necessarily found God."[11] God the creator is a God of love; and, whether Dawkins likes this or not, a loving God needs to be described in personal language. The personal language describing God, I add, is symbolic language, not literal. What Dawkins is asking for is a literal description of God's role in natural processes. He wants to find God in the equations. A loving God described in personal language will simply not show up in the equations. If it is a requirement that God be found in the equations, and if God does not show up there, one can understand why atheism might be the conclusion drawn.

Dawkins seems like a fisherman having a bad day. He baits his hook. He throws his line in the water. Nothing bites on his worm. So, he concludes there are no fish in the lake. Because he looks for God in the equations and fails to find God there, he concludes no God is to be found anywhere.

Atheist Liberation from Religion

If the atheist crusade against outmoded religious belief succeeds, then the gain will be a new form of freedom. Michael Shermer, publisher of *Skeptic* magazine, gives witness to the powerful attraction of atheistic liberty. "The conjuncture of losing my religion, finding science, and discovering glorious contingency was remarkably empowering and liberating. It gave me a sense of joy and freedom. Freedom to think for myself....With the knowledge that his may be all there is, and that I can trigger my own cascading changes, I was free to live life to its fullest."[12] Note how science has replaced religion, for Shermer; and this has led to freedom of thought and control over his own life changes. Religion oppresses. Science liberates. This is the message of evangelical atheism.

Science is messianic, proclaim the evangelical atheists, as if they owned an exclusive patent. Yet, they patently do not. The materialist worldview they espouse is in fact an ideological add-on, a superimposition. Atheism is not inherent to scientific inquiry itself. For Dawkins to apotheosize natural selection within evolutionary theory is simply unwarranted, as many religious Darwinists would attest. Perhaps Nancey Murphy speaks for the pro-science Christian when she writes, "I am not at all sympathetic with any of the antievolution movements, but I am sympathetic with theists who object to the promotion, in the name of science, of materialistic worldviews."[13] Murphy disavows the illegitimate move Dawkins makes from his science to his theological judgment, namely, there is no God. Marilynne Robinson concludes, "Dawkins's critique of religion cannot properly be called scientific."[14]

Michael Ruse, in partial contrast to these critics, argues that Dawkins is actually a theological ally, not an enemy. Beyond his surface atheism, Dawkins provides a way in which Christian theology can connect with the Darwinian model of evolution. Development if not progress is the connector; and the human race develops into something unique, special. "Dawkins is an evolutionary progressionist who thinks that humans emerged naturally and predictably from the way of evolution—at least, predictably in the sense that the processes of evolution keep pushing organisms up the scale and consciousness is at the top of the scale. And that, I take it, is just what the Christian needs."[15] Dawkins, according to Ruse, is paradoxically supporting Christian claims regarding the eminent place to which the human race as evolved in nature. Human beings are special; and evolution has made us special.

What I appreciate about the new breed of atheists is their strong advocacy for natural science. The pursuit of scientific inquiry feeds the human soul hungry for knowledge. Yet, I object to the unnecessary ideology of materialism which they attach to science. Rather than admit that their atheistic commitment is an act of faith, they attempt to borrow the prestige of science to buttress their cause. The problem is that science belongs to all of us, not merely to the atheists among us.

Religious Pluralism as Description

Aggressive atheism is not the only competitor for the religious niche. Religious pluralists are also vying for the same niche. And, like the atheists, pluralists believe their own beliefs are more fit than traditional beliefs in a personal God when associated with fundamentalist or absolutist religion. Although the majority of pluralists are liberal Protestants or liberal Roman Catholics, the position could in principle garner disciples from any of the world's sophisticated religious traditions. Like the atheists, the pluralists would like to bring peace among warring religious groups. Unlike the atheists, who deny respect to every religious belief system, the pluralists believe the way to peace is through respecting everyone's beliefs equally. So, it appears that these two, atheism and pluralism, are opposites. Well, at least this is the way it appears. A closer look, however, will show that atheism and pluralism share some fundamental commitments, including disrespect for tradition-specific religious beliefs.

Now, before we proceed, let me clarify the term we are using here, *pluralism*. As a *description*, this term describes the current cultural situation in which people from a diversity of religious traditions live together and work together. As a *prescription*, this term prescribes adherence to an ideology with two fundamental principles: first, metaphysically, all religious beliefs are finite perspectives on a single trans-finite reality; and, second, ethically, because members of competing religious traditions are morally obligated to recognize the equality or parity of alternative religious viewpoints. By adhering to these two principles, pluralists hope that we can bring peace between otherwise competing religions. It is pluralism in the prescriptive or ideological form that makes it a contender for the religious niche in contemporary culture.

At minimum, ideological pluralism "requires that the student of religion recognize the inherent power and validity of each tradition in its own terms,"[16] are the words of John Cobb. The next step is to attribute parity or equality to every religious tradition, denying the superiority of one's own tradition. Finally, at maximum, presecriptive or ideological pluralism typically posits that each religion is revelatory or even salvific, albeit in historically conditioned and relative ways.

Although the word "pluralism" is the one most frequently used to identify this school of thought, the position can also be described as the "parity model" or the "mutuality model." Paul Knitter describes it this way: "proponents of this model presume…'rough parity' among religions. That doesn't mean that all the religions are the same or that they are equal in every respect. But it does mean that they all have 'equal rights' to speak and be heard, based on their inherent value. So this model is uncomfortable with, and seeks to avoid, any claims that one religion has a pre-given (especially if it's a God-given) superiority over all the others that makes it 'final' or 'absolute' or 'unsurpassable' over all the others."[17] Over against the particular religious traditions we have inherited from history, the model of religious pluralism looks for a common denominator or, more, a higher or more universal form of the sacred which could absorb the array of culturally specific images of the divine.

Langdon Gilkey's later thought may provide an example of the parity model. By "some sort of parity" he means "the elimination of our assumption of unquestioned or a priori superiority of our religion…it is this new attitude that I name *plurality*."[18] As a theologian, Gilkey can grant parity within plurality because he acknowledges "the presence of healing grace and truth in other communions."[19] The pluralistic model is itself a theological position that attributes genuine revelation to multiple religious traditions; and, on this basis, ideological pluralism grounds an ethic of respect for religious rights in the larger social order. What pluralists oppose is religious imperialism, the military conquering or even the cultural colonizing of one religious tradition by another. The chief weapon against such imperialists is a new theology, a pluralistic theology that grounds religious unity across traditional lines.

John Hick, for whom the one God has many names, provides us with perhaps the definitive example of such a new theology. He explores what he calls the "pluralistic hypothesis," which holds that "the great world faiths embody different perceptions and conceptions of, and correspondingly different responses to, the Real from within the major variant ways of being human; and that within each of them the transformation of human existence from self-centeredness to Reality-centeredness is taking place."[20] Hick's term, "the Real," designates what others mean when speaking of God, the Sacred, the transcendent, the ultimate reality, and such. When persons claim experiences of revelation, Hick refuses to call them "illusory." Rather, "they are empirically, that is experientially, real as authentic manifestations of the real."[21] On the basis of the pluralistic hypothesis described this way, Hick finds two reasons why we should respect the beliefs of all the world's great religions. First, being religious is being human. Each religion formulates in its own culturally specific way what it means to be a human being. Second, the plurality of cultural perspectives on what he calls "the Real" does not obviate the fact that the Real is communicating with human minds. What persons experience as the transcendent is, in fact, the transcendent Sacred in manifestation.

Some non-atheistic Social Darwinists tend to work out of a framework of religious pluralism like the one we have been describing. Religion evolves like everything else, they say. Having begun with primitive superstition, religion has advanced to monotheism, mysticism, rationalism, and then finally transcended itself by becoming science. Each religious tradition provides a relative perspective on the absolute mystery, on the single force that gives nature its energy and form. The late nineteenth century philosopher most responsible for Social Darwinism, Herbert Spencer, puts it this way: "Religions diametrically opposed in their overt dogmas, are yet perfectly at one in the tacit conviction that this existence of the world with all it contains and all which surrounds it, is a mystery ever pressing for interpretation. On this point, if on no other, there is entire unanimity."[22] Beneath the diversity of dogmas there is unity in the reality reflected by the dogmas.

Religious Pluralism as Prescription

Pluralism as a prescriptive ideology seeks to combat a tendency within religion to absolutize what is relative—that is, to absolutize a particular perspective on what is transcendent. For both metaphysical and ethical reasons, pluralists affirm all religious claims in order to combat absolute religious claims. David Ray Griffin describes the agenda of generic religious pluralism in terms of a twofold affirmation, one negative and the other positive. "The negative affirmation is the rejection of religious absolutism, which means rejecting the a priori assumption that their own religion is the only one that provides saving truths and values to its adherents, that it alone is divinely inspired, that it has been divinely established as the only legitimate religion, intended to replace all others. The positive affirmation, which goes beyond the negative one, is the acceptance of the idea that there are indeed religions other than one's own that provide saving truths and values to their adherents."[23] Such religious pluralism is motivated by an ethical urgency, namely, the need for inter-religious cooperation to address the threats to peace on earth. "We must find a solution to our global problems, especially the problems of war, imperialism, weapons of mass destruction, global apartheid, massive human rights violations, genocide, and the ecological crisis."[24] By showing respect based on parity to religions other than one's own, by showing disrespect to religions that absolutize their respective perspectives, pluralists can work for cooperation across religious lines to provide a united front when tackling these ethical challenges.

Thus, withdrawing the religious warrant for violence is as important to the pluralists as it is for the atheists. Harvard's Gordon D. Kaufman identifies himself with "humanistic theism," and he tries to launch a criticism of traditional Christianity from this vantage point. "It is important that Christians never forget that the crusades against those regarded as infidel Muslims were conducted in the name of the crucified one, and the tortures of the Inquisition were intended to compel submission to precisely a church that claimed to be the exclusive mediator of Christ's salvation. These sorts of actions and claims, of which Christians have often been guilty, far from promoting the humane order for which Jesus died, have further undermined it by dividing humans from each other instead of reconciling them, by setting them at war with each other instead of bringing peace."[25]

This leads to a more general commitment: fight fundamentalism. "Today fundamentalistic reifications of religious positions appear around the globe with increasing frequency, offering religious legitimation for dangerously parochial social and ethnic movements and practices that, in their divisiveness and destructiveness, are a threat to all humanity. We need a way to understand our religiousness that can honor the integrity and meaning of each religious tradition and yet open it to an appreciation of and reconciliation with others."[26] In other words, if we can stop the fundamentalists, then we can stop religiously inspired violence. This is the social goal within the conceptual model of religious pluralism.

What is the step that must be taken to move our global society from religious violence to religious peace? Answer: we must convert the leaders of specific religious traditions to pluralism. This is how Kaufman recommends such a conversion. "If the great religious traditions could come to understand their deepest insights and truth in the historical and pluralistic way I am proposing...that is, as contributions to the ongoing larger conversation of humankind on the deepest issues with which life confronts us humans—we would move a step further toward finding a way to live together on our small planet as a single, though pluriform, humanity."[27] What Kaufman is asking religious leaders to do is subordinate their specific religious insight to Kaufman's "larger conversation."

This plan is doomed to fail, it seems to me; because the very religious traditions Kaufman is inviting to the conversation each hold to some level of definitive or absolute truth. Can we honestly ask someone with such a belief to subordinate that belief to one espoused by Hick or Kaufman or some other pluralist? To convert to pluralism would be to deny one's tradition-specific commitment, at least in principle.

Yet, pluralists persist. Here's the logic: if each person could surrender what is essential to his or her religious claim to truth, then they could join the club of religious pluralists. If every one of the world's religious traditions would join this club, then religious rivalry and hence violence would cease. This attempt to convert tradition-specific believers into pluralists uncovers a contradiction within the pluralist agenda. On the one hand, the way to combat religious absolutism is to respect the claims of rival religions. On the other hand, the way to combat religious absolutism is to deny respect to those who disagree with the pluralists, namely, the absolutists. So goes the theory.

Might we see an alliance between the pluralists and the atheists? After all, they both want to overcome the violent expressions of religion due to belief in a personal God with its accompanying absolutism and fundamentalism. However, atheists show disdain for the pluralists. Referring to religious pluralists as "liberals" or "moderates," atheists object to the gentle respect shown for otherwise ridiculous or even dangerous religious doctrines. Sam Harris, for example, denounces such tolerance of unacceptable religious views. "Tolerance is not without its problems. Our fear of provoking religious hatred has rendered us unwilling to criticize ideas that are increasingly maladaptive and patently ridiculous."[28]

Yet, a closer look will show that the pluralist position is much closer to the atheist position than one might at first suspect. Why? Because each representative of a traditional religious position must give up reliance upon the definitiveness of his or her religious perspective in order to join the pluralist club. Despite what they say, members of the pluralist club do not in fact respect the positions articulated by each religion's specific theology. Kaufman is able to admit this. "For the *authoritarian* and *absolutistic* characteristics of traditional religious truth-claims are not, in fact, given full respect in this more democratic, open, dialogical understanding."[29] On the surface, atheists and pluralists appear to be polar opposites. But when the dust settles, they both hold the same disrespect toward the specific claims of each specific religious tradition.

Could one modify this pluralist position to show respect for differing religious claims even if they seem distasteful? Perhaps Diana Eck, chair of Harvard's pluralism project, might provide a laudable example. Eck employs the metaphor of a "world house," within which live differing religious perspectives as a single family. Together they engage one another, seeking to understand one another in their differences. The Eck method differs from the Hick method of subordinating the differing perspectives to a transcendent Real. "Religious pluralism is not primarily about common ground," she writes. "Pluralism takes the reality of difference as its starting point. The challenge of pluralism is...to discover ways of living, connecting, relating, arguing, and disagreeing in a society of differences."[30] With Eck's version of prescriptive pluralism, respect for what is particular in each religion remains more possible.

Let us make it more difficult: could one modify the pluralist position to show respect for some religious claims yet show disrespect for other such claims? Within the pluralistic model, some theologians do wish to recognize differences, and even evaluate some differences as better than others. Respect for everyone else's point of view need not erase entirely one's critical faculties. Following Hick with a slight demure is Paul O. Ingram, who leaves us with such a caution. "The idea that the religious traditions of the world are culturally and historically limited responses to a single reality that each names differently does not inherently imply that all religious traditions teach the same things or are equally true or equally valid responses to the Sacred. There is much in all religious traditions that is nonsense. The truth claims of some religious traditions may be closer approximations than others…"[31] Perhaps with this modification some pluralists and some atheists could justify an alliance against just those religious traditions they disrespect, namely, the fundamentalist strain within many larger religious traditions.

What I appreciate about most religious pluralists is their implicit ethic of protecting the rights of all religious traditions in our observably pluralistic world. When exclusivist claims made by aggressive religions lead to cultural imperialism if not military imperialism, the rights of colonized religious believers are squashed right along with their beliefs. Pluralists defend these rights, and rightly so.

However, the theoretical ground for such defense of religious rights takes its own form of colonization. Pluralists are like worms burrowing within religious fruit, changing its taste. On the one hand, pluralists extend the hand of respect toward each established religious tradition. Yet, as soon as that tradition exhibits any signs of exclusivity, the respecting hand is withdrawn. In effect, adherents to the existing world religions are being asked to convert to pluralism from within their own tradition; and this implies in some cases a sacrifice of their own strongest commitments to beliefs regarding the ultimately Real. The prescriptive pluralist position collapses under the weight of its own self-contradiction.

The prescriptive pluralist position especially collapses in the face of Islam, where belief in the Real of which John Hick speaks is already a tradition-specific belief. What the pluralist believes and what the Muslim believes about the Real are virtually the same. Yet the pluralist uses this belief in two ways, both to respect Islam and to ask Islam to convert from exclusivity to pluralism. The lack of coherence becomes visible when the pluralist position is put to the test of actually respecting tradition-specific religious claims.

Islam and the "Real" God

Islam champions the oneness of God. It also champions God's transcendent essence, an essence that lies beyond all attributes and even beyond what has been revealed to us about God. Islamic piety bows in humble reverence and total submission before Allah, the most sublime, the most majestic, the most awesome.

A Muslim in good conscience must compete with atheists and pluralists for the religious niche. The atheist must be mistaken, thinks the Muslim, because God exists. There is more. God's existence comes prior to our own existence, and is the source of our existence. God is more real than we are. To deny God's existence would be blasphemous.

For two different reasons, the pluralist must also be mistaken, according to the Muslim. First, the model of religious pluralism asks us to tolerate if not accept a wide variety of belief systems, each with a separate god or goddess or even a pantheon of divinities; and this tolerance constitutes a form of subjective polytheism. Second, all these beliefs are wrong. The definitive, absolute, and unsurpassable revelation is found in one decisive location, the Qur'an. The *Shahada* or Muslim confession states this without ambiguity or compromise: "There is no god but Allah, and Muhammad is his prophet." For non-Muslims to respect the Muslim religion, they must respect this religious tradition in its exclusivist self-understanding. Neither atheism nor pluralism is capable of this.

To think of God as the transcendent creator of all things leads contemporary Islamic theology into conflict not just with atheism, but also with the Western natural science claimed by the new atheists as their support. Muslims object because the scientist pursues knowledge of this material world without reference to its creator, God. God does not appear in scientific equations, and this bothers some Muslims. Seyyed Hossein Nasr trumpets rhetorical questions. "How can Islam accept any form of knowledge that is not rooted in God and does not necessarily lead to Him? How can it explain the universe without ever referring to the Transcendent Cause of all things, of which the Noble Qur'an speaks on almost every page?"[32]

If Muslims belong to a theological club with more than one member, it would be monotheism. Divine oneness is central. This means all polytheisms or even sympathies with polytheism are eschewed. "Choose not two gods. There is only One God. So of Me, Me only, be in awe" (Qur'an 16:51). To flirt with polytheism or even to entertain suggestions that any being could receive even a share of our worship would be to commit *shirk*, to illegitimately associate any partner with God. *Shirk* is a blasphemous form of sin.

Tawhid characterizes the Muslim's spiritual disposition as well as theological commitment. *Tawhid* is the activity of asserting or affirming the unity of God, of Allah. The very activity of asserting God's oneness disposes the Muslim to live in proper relationship to God. And because God is the "real"—the "Real" is one of God's hundred names—living *Tawhid* draws a person into reality. *Tawhid* leads us to become fully human. In contrast, to commit *shirk*—that is, to associate something or someone with the one God and to compromise the unity of God—is to remove oneself from the "real" and drop into a state that is less than fully human.

The oneness of God has two dimensions, one exclusive and the other inclusive. The exclusive unity emphasizes that God is unique. Nothing is like God. God is absolutely other, holy. God is the creator, and nothing within creation rivals God. The inclusive unity of God refers to the unifying impact God has on all of reality. All things find their reality in the one God. If we ask a Muslim, "where in the world is God?", he or she would likely answer: "God is not *in* the world; but the entire world finds its unity and reality in God."

Islam and the Trinity

What this implies, further, is that no plurality within the single divine life is acceptable. The idea of anything like human family relations within God's life must be excluded. "Say: He is Allah, the One! Allah, the eternally Besought of all! He begetteth not nor was begotten. And there is none comparable unto Him" (Qur'an 112). Badru D. Kateregga says that "Islam makes clear that God has no son, no father, brother, sister, wife, or daughters. The pre-Islamic idea of calling goddesses daughters of Allah was condemned by the Prophet."[33] The rejection here of begetting accomplished two things within the original seventh century context of Arabia. It repudiated flatly any syncretism with previously existing polytheistic traditions. In addition, by repudiating the idea of divine sonship, Islam repudiated the Christian concepts of incarnation and Trinity.

Here is the definitive passage, wherein the Christian doctrine of the Trinity is confronted. "The Messiah, Jesus son of Mary, was only the Messenger of God, and His Word that He committed to Mary, and a Spirit from Him. So have faith in God and His messengers, and do not say 'Three'. Refrain, better it is for you. God is only One God" (Qur'an 4:171).

Now, curiously, just what Trinity is being rejected here? Is it the Trinity of Father, Son, and Holy Spirit? Not exactly. The Qur'an seems to assume that the Christian Trinity consists of God, Jesus, and Mary. "And when God said, 'O Jesus son of Mary, didst thou say unto men, 'Take me and my mother as gods, apart from God'?' He said, 'To Thee be glory! It is not mine to say what I have no right to'" (Qur'an 5:116). Given that the Qur'an appeared in the late seventh century in the part of the world where Eastern Christianity was widely known, perhaps the new religion was reacting against Mary understood as *theotokos* or "Mother of God." Perhaps it was Mariology that prompted this anti-trinitarianism. If so, then the Qur'an misunderstands Christian theology, even though popular Christian piety may have been appropriately perceived. Be that as it may, this is a historical speculation. The theological agenda regarding divine oneness and the Trinity remains.

Mark Swanson observes that "this misunderstanding mattered little. Later Muslim thinkers were equally mystified and offended by more technically correct expositions of the Christian Trinity."[34] At best, Muslims find Christian Trinitarian theology confusing; at worst, tri-theism. "The Christians have followed a procedure which has obliged them to proclaim the existence, conceptually and objectively, of three Gods," writes al-Ghazali.[35] By violating divine oneness when imputing threeness, Christians are guilty of *shirk*.

The problems with Trinitarian thinking are multiple, from an Islamic point of view. First, the strict oneness of God denies all plurality within divinity. This oneness is a simple oneness, in the philosophical sense of simplicity. Second, because all plurality belongs to this world and not to the divine realm, for worshippers to treat the plurality of divine manifestations as themselves divine is to commit *shirk*. Third, to treat God as "Father" is to so humanize God as to functionally deny God's transcendence to all that is human. Fourth, because God is not a family man, so to speak, it makes no sense to speak of Jesus as the "Son of God." And, fifth, the suffering of the Son could not result in the suffering of the Father. Jesus' suffering was this-worldly only. God is beyond passion, beyond suffering. Muslims reject patripassianism.

The astute Kenneth Cragg recommends that when Christians interpret their beliefs to Muslims, they should ask Muslims to "ponder the Christian Trinity, not as a violation of Unity, but as a form of its expression. We cannot proceed except on the understanding that we are both firmly and equally believers that God is One. We both stand squarely in the Hebrew tradition: 'The Lord our Lord is ONE Lord'."[36] Yet, this might not be as easy as it sounds. The unity of which Christians speak is a complex unity, a oneness of three persons: Father, Son, and Holy Spirit. If Islam, in contrast, insists that Allah's unity is simple, then this complex unity internal to the divine life would still be unacceptable.

Muslims and Christians in Dialogue

Roman Catholics at the Second Vatican Council (1962-1965) could say they hold Muslims "with esteem. They adore one God, living and enduring, merciful and all-powerful, Maker of heaven and earth."[37] Catholics and Muslims can both find internal to their respective theological visions an apprehension of the single sublime mystery. They do not need pluralists from the outside to tell them that their respective finite perspectives need to be supplanted by doctrine of a greater Real. Theologians within these two religious traditions can speak with one another directly; they know they share a fundamental understanding of the one God.

Nevertheless, Christian apologists should not give up on the Trinity. They should press on, seeking growth in shared understanding. Locating genuine if subtle differences within shared understanding becomes the next task.

David Shenk, who presses the dialogue forward while identifying the subtle nuances, distinguishes two types of revelation. For Islam, what is revealed is God's will, not God's being. For Christianity, what is revealed is God in Godself. "The Qur'an stresses the revelation of God's commands and His names to humans. In the Bible we perceive God as the One Who reveals Himself to humankind.... Yahweh reveals not only His will, commands, and names to humankind, but also Himself in personal self-disclosure.... God gives Himself in suffering, redemptive love. Because of His love, He sorrows when we sorrow, He suffers when we suffer, He is pained by our sin. God loves us totally."[38] What Shenk is describing here is the economic Trinity—that is, God engaging the world. The suffering of the Son is taken up into the divine life. And through the Spirit all our experiences of suffering are felt equally by God, the one who loves totally and unconditionally. Even though Christian systematic theologians have historically striven to protect the first person of the Trinity from patripassianism, clearly the thrust of Shenk's position is that the sufferings of the world are empathetically shared by God. I find myself applauding Shenk at this point.

What is at stake is the question: is God graciously and lovingly involved with creatures in the world? For some Christians, the symbol of God as "Father" connotes this divine caring for us in our finite world. Alain Besançon, for example, distinguishes Islam from Christianity on this point. "Although Muslims like to enumerate the 99 names of God, missing from the list, but central to the Jewish and even more so to the Christian conception of God, is 'Father'—i.e., a personal God capable of a reciprocal and loving relation with men....The Muslim god is utterly impassive, to ascribe loving feelings to Him would be suspect."[39]

Kateregga finds exactly this idea of divine involvement in our world to be suspect. He raises objections to the symbol of the Father within Trinitarian thought. To ascribe fatherhood to God risks humanizing God. God is not literally a Father. And we ought not to consider hypostases such as the Son or Spirit as equally divine. Trinitarian thinking de-divinizes God, so it appears. "God, according to Muslim witness, is absolute and transcendent.... God is not to be conceived as having human form or attributes.... A Muslim cannot invoke him in the name of the Father, Son, or Holy Spirit. All the divine attributes are well embedded in his perfect unity." The divine essence, it is assumed here, transcends the attributes we perceive in the divine manifestations. From an Islamic point of view, Christians fail to distinguish God's attributes from God's essence, an essence which transcends these attributes.

Yet, a Christian might counter, that the language of Father, Son, and Spirit is symbolic, not conceptual. The being of God, according to Christian theology, transcends these symbolic images. This places Islamic and Christian thinking closer, even though still not isomorphic. Shenk responds to Kateregga: "When Christians refer to God as Father, they should not think of God as being human. Christians share with Muslims the prohibition against conceiving of God in the form of an image."[40] Shenk is correct in saying that Christians, like Muslims, affirm that the reality of God transcends our symbolic language of God. The images we have of God are metaphorical, not literal. Nevertheless, Christians believe that God is involved in the world, that God loves the world and engages the world with gracious involvement. A sublime ontology of divine transcendence can not become an excuse for sacrificing the personal involvement of God in the world, a Christian would want to contend.

Not all conversation between Muslims and Christians needs to be focused on such differences. "When Christians and Muslims talk bout God, they are talking about the same God," writes Kateregga.[41] According to Mark Swanson, "Shared belief in one creator God—who reveals his will to human beings, who hears their prayers, and who will raise the dead on the Last Day—enables Christian and Muslim neighbors and co-workers throughout the world to share texts and experiences, explain practices, and reflect on what it means to live a human life in God's sight, to God's honor."[42]

That our human life could be characterized by love of God and love of neighbor became the theme of an extraordinary historical initiative taken in late 2007 by 138 Muslim scholars representing all branches of Islam. This group issued and open theological letter to Christian leaders that emphasized what these two religions plus Judaism hold in common, namely, the commandment to love God and love neighbor. "Muslims and Christians together make up well over half of the world's population," opens the letter, *A Common Word between Us and You*. "Without peace and justice between these two religious communities, there can be no meaningful peace in the world.... The basis for this peace and understanding already exists. It is part of the very foundational principles of both faiths: love of the One God, and love of the neighbor."[43]

Of the top of the list of things which I most appreciate about Islam, we find authentic humility in respect to the majesty and glory of God. The ninety nine names Muslims use to refer to God each protect the heavenly mystery; so that we become conscious of God while resisting the temptation to tread on the holy. Yet, what seems to be inherent in the New Testament revelation is divine involvement in the world. God as Father cares for earth's creatures. God as Son suffers, dies, and undergoes resurrection. God as Spirit calls, gathers, and enlightens. God is active in the world, active in the hearts and lives of persons of faith. Somehow, this active presence of God needs some theological accounting for that Trinitarian thinking is able to supply.

Could Islam Embrace Pluralism?

Contemporary Muslims are caught between monolithic Islamic countries where religion and state are unified, on the one hand, and the lure of democratic societies which separate church and state, on the other hand. It appears that the idea of religious pluralism can flourish only in the latter, but not the former.

"Here I take religious pluralism to mean the acknowledgement of the intrinsic redemptive value of competing religious traditions," writes Abdulaziz Sachedina at the University of Virginia. "It is expected, however, that beliefs and values essential to one community will contravene those of others; herein lurks the potential for conflict and violence."[44] Sachedina recognizes that the absolutism of Islam appears to be irreconcilable with the concept of religious tolerance or the ideology of pluralism. It seems to be, at least.

Yet, he asks: are there resources within Islam itself that could provide a "fresh" review of the heritage and re-dispose Islam toward freedom of religion? Yes, he responds. Sachedina's interpretation of the Qur'an is that Islamic society could organize itself around two jurisdictions, one in the horizontal direction of law for the common good and the other at the in the vertical dimension of a person's relationship to God. After all, one's internal heartfelt decision for or against the claim of faith cannot be enforced by external law. This concept of double jurisdiction would allow an Islamic state to permit freedom of religion within it.

This double jurisdiction is based upon a double source of revelation, the moral law which comes to us in creation and the divine law which comes to us through the special revelation of the Qur'an. "God provides two forms of guidance: universal moral guidance that touches all humans *qua* humans, and particular revelatory guidance that is given to a specific faith community. On the basis of universal guidance, it is conceivable to demand uniformity because an objective and universally binding moral standard is assumed to exist that guarantees true human well-being....However, on the basis of particular guidance through scripture, it is crucial to allow human beings to exercise their volition in matters of personal faith...This clarification regarding the two forms of guidance that the Qur'an speaks about provides us with a scriptural basis for freedom of religion."[45]

What we see here is a conscientious struggle from within the parameters of an absolutist religious tradition—the kind of religious tradition opposed by both atheists and pluralists—to accommodate and even embrace social structures that would bring peace between rival religious traditions.

How Hot is the Competition?

Despite the admirable search for religious tolerance and peaceful co-existence, the competition between these three—atheism, pluralism, and Islam—is red hot. The fire ants of atheism are eating at the roots of religion, all religion. A line between good and evil is being drawn, with atheism on the good side and religion on the evil side. Religion incites war, says Susan Blackmore, extending Dawkins' arguments. "The history of warfare is largely a history of people killing each other for religious reasons."[46]

Among the atheists who see religion as unambiguously evil are Christopher Hitchens and Sam Harris. According to atheist Hitchens, "four irreducible objections to religious faith" obtain, namely,[47] "that it wholly misrepresents the origins of man and the cosmos, that because of this original error it manages to combine the maximum of servility with the maximum of solipsism, that it is both the result and cause of dangerous sexual repression, and that it is ultimately grounded on wish-thinking." Hitchens assumes that "the attitude of religion to science is always necessarily problematic and very often necessarily hostile."[48] Although Hitchens might hope that we would simply evolve ourselves right up and out of religion into an epoch of scientific reason, he finds himself unable to be optimistic. "Religious faith is, precisely *because* we are still-evolving creatures, ineradicable."[49] Hitchens' complaint is the religion poisons everything in the human way of life. Even if we cannot rid ourselves of religion, Hitchens can dream of a society without it.

The complaint raised by Sam Harris is that "religious faith remains a perpetual source of human conflict."[50] In order to bring global peace, we need to stamp out religion. The religions Harris particularly wants to eliminate are Islam, Christianity, and Judaism. These irrational and violence prone holdovers from a pre-modern era must be dispensed with. "All reasonable men and women have a common enemy....Our enemy is nothing other than faith itself."[51]

Islam sits atop Harris' hit list. Don't think it is only the "extremists" who are a danger to society, warns Harris. Islam at its core is violent. "The idea that Islam is a 'peaceful religion hijacked by extremists' is a fantasy...because most Muslims are *utterly deranged by their religious faith.*"[52]

Why does Harris go after the core of Islam and not just those we think of as extremists? Harris contends that the foundational book, the Qur'an, thought to be literally the word of God, teaches devout Muslims to commit themselves to holy war against all non-Muslims. Harris cites one dangerous passage after another, such as, "The only true faith in God's sight is Islam.... He that denies God's revelations should know that swift is God's reckoning" (Qur'an 3:19). The Qur'an and its concept of *jihad* or holy war are essential not just for suicide bombers, but for all devout Muslims. "On almost every page," writes Harris, the Koran instructs observant Muslims to despise non-believers. On almost every page, it prepares the ground for religious conflict....Islam, more than any other religion human beings have devised, has all the makings of a thoroughgoing cult of death."[53] According to Harris, this cult of death gets additional energy from teaching young men that, if they become a suicide bomber, they will go straight to paradise, avoid the judgment, and receive a reward of seventy virgins for their pleasure. What can we expect from a religious teaching such as this? "The only future devout Muslims can envisage—*as Muslims*—is one in which all infidels have been converted to Islam, subjugated, or killed."[54]

After drawing this picture of Islam as the cult of death, Harris prescribes what Western civilization should do to defend itself. First, we should teach rationality. We should teach our children to think critically, to evaluate religious claims on the basis of evidence. Once we have examined religious beliefs, they will be seen to be unfounded. We will emerge from our outmoded faith into the freedom of a truly liberal society. If teaching reason is less than adequate, however, then we should move toward a second form of self-defense.

We need to ask: will this gradual conversion from irrational religion to rational atheism move fast enough to prevent inundation by the Islamic menace? Can we pass through the transition before Muslims get their hands on nuclear or biological weapons? Perhaps not. Might pre-emptive self-defense be called for? Yes, says Harris. This threat might even call for a nuclear first strike. "The only thing likely to ensure our survival may be a nuclear first strike of our own. Needless to say, this would be an unthinkable crime—as it would kill tens of millions of innocent civilians in a single day—but it may be the only course of action available to us, given what Islamists believe."[55] Harris is giving expression to Western anxiety, to fear; and this leads him to propose his own form of atheist jihad against Islam. "The West must either win the argument or win the war. All else will be bondage."[56]

If religious peace is the objective, might a tactic other than Harris' be equally effective while avoiding a bloody counter jihad? Might the religious pluralists be able to persuade Muslims to be peaceful through respecting Islamic beliefs? If Muslims receive respect from the West, might this mitigate their hostility? No, says Harris. Referring to pluralists as "religious moderates," Harris indicts them as part of the problem. By respecting Islam's literalism, religious moderates tacitly approve of Muslim belligerency.

Dawkins agrees. "I do everything in my power to warn people against faith itself, not just against so-called 'extremist' faith. The teachings of 'moderate' religion, though not extremist in themselves, are an open invitation to extremism."[57] Dawkins continues: "Suicide bombers do what they do because they really believe what they were taught in their religious schools; that duty to God exceeds all other priorities, and that martyrdom in his service will be rewarded in the gardens of Paradise."[58] The very tolerance shown by moderates—read 'religious pluralists'—imputes respect to religious fundamentalists and extremists who do not deserve that respect.

Respect for Islam is not effective. What we need is a critical examination of both Islam and Christianity; but the moderates do not have the backbone to launch this criticism. "They do not want anything too critical said about people who *really* believe in the God of their fathers, because tolerance, perhaps above all else, is sacred. To speak plainly and truthfully about the state of our world—to say, for instance, that the Bible and the Koran both contain mountains of life-destroying gibberish—is antithetical to tolerance as moderates currently conceive it. But we can no longer afford the luxury of such political correctness. We must finally recognize the price we are paying to maintain the iconography of our ignorance."[59]

On the one hand, it must be said of the pluralists (or religious moderates) that they are as opposed to scriptural literalism as is Harris or Dawkins. Pluralists have no tolerance for fundamentalism in either Christianity or Islam. Conservative representatives within most religious traditions stay away from pluralists because of this. So, it would be inaccurate of Harris or Dawkins to imply that moderates actually encourage either literalism or violence. On the other hand, pluralists are not nearly as evangelical or aggressive as the new breed of atheists. They do not advocate their own version of jihad to stamp out the fundamentalism they equally abhor. The atheists will not tolerate tolerant bystanders: either join in the anti-religious crusade or be identified as part of the enemy.

Atheism and Genocide

Now, let us ask: if we could subject anachronistic religious traditions to criticism and begin to govern our civilization on atheistic principles, would we establish a society of peace, justice, and love? Do atheists have a record of higher virtue than religious people? Not according to history. Here is one description. "The most horrible genocidal atrocities of the past century and, indeed, in recorded history, Hitler's Holocaust in Central Europe, Stalin's purge of non-Communists in the former Soviet Union and Eastern Bloc, and the Khmer Rouge's killing fields in Cambodia (which currently holds the record for the largest number of human casualties) were all perpetrated in the name of atheistic ideologies that made no provisions for an afterlife and were sometimes directed at eliminating those who believed in an afterlife. What more compelling evidence could there be that it is misguided to point the finger of blame for this or other humanly perpetrated atrocities at religion per se or at the belief in some form of life after death?"[60]

Harris has heard such criticisms of atheism before. He believes he can dismiss them because these genocides were perpetrated not by true rationalists but by rationalists contaminated by ideology. Stalin and Mao were victims of Marxist ideology. And Nazism was not genuine atheism, because it fed off Christian anti-Semitism. "Nazis were agents of religion."[61] Even if atheists perpetrated genocide, we can still say atheism is scientific and good while religion is unscientific and bad.

Dawkins responds similarly, by saying that Stalin's atrocities were due not to his atheism but to his Marxism; and Hitler was probably a Catholic influenced by Martin Luther's anti-Semitism that relied upon the theory of eugenics. Curious. "Stalin was an atheist and Hitler probably wasn't but even if he was, the bottom line of the Stalin/Hitler debating point is very simple. Individual atheists may do evil things but they don't do evil things in the name of atheism. Stalin and Hitler did extremely evil things, in the name of, respectively, dogmatic and doctrinaire Marxism, and an insane and unscientific eugenics theory tinged with sub-Wagnerian ravings. Religious wars really are fought in the name of religion, and they have been horribly frequent in history."[62] Even though atheists are responsible for genocide on a horrendous scale, the Marxist and Nazi perpetrators belong to the equivalent of a different sect or denomination of atheism, not the scientific kind of atheism Dawkins and Harris espouse. In short, a specifically scientific, rational, critical form of atheism would not, once in power, engage in genocide; rather, it would eliminate the atrocities of both religion and the unorthodox forms of historical atheism. This seems to be the position advocated here by the new evangelical atheists.

Marilynne Robinson is not persuaded by Dawkins' attempt to exonerate atheism by extricating science from Nazi genocide. Even though anti-Semitism certainly predated the rise of Darwinism, during the second decade of the twentieth century it was at such a low ebb that it had virtually no active influence on German society. It bordered on the forgotten. What happened then was that Hitler adopted Darwinian eugenics into his program of racial hygiene; and within the eugenic theory he redefined the "Jew" in genetic or racial rather than religious terms. Hitler produced a scientized racism. The winds of the *Zeitgeist* then began to blow in the direction of genocide. It was science, not religion, that propelled Nazi Germany toward the holocaust, says Robinson. "To Dawkins's objection that Nazi science was not authentic science I would reply, first, that neither Nazis nor Germans had any monopoly on these theories, which were influential throughout the Western world, and second, that the research on human subjects carried out by those holding such assumptions was good enough science to appear in medical texts for fully half a century. This is not to single out science as exceptionally inclined to do harm, though its capacity for doing harm is by now unequaled. It is only to note that science, too, is implicated in this bleak human proclivity, and is one major instrument of it."[63] In short, to identify atheism with pure science in order to distance it from the Nazi atrocities fails in its attempt to persuade us that a scientized atheism would usher in human virtue and world peace.

Is Islam Really Irrational and Violent?

Now, just what do the Muslims think about all of this? How much ducking do Muslims need to do in the face of shots fired from atheists and pluralists? Are Muslims irremediably irrational? Certainly not, says Basit Bilal Koshul. Belief in God is founded on faith, which is a kind of feeling, to be sure; yet, as St. Anselm would say, Islamic faith seeks understanding. This understanding is cognitive, rational, and even scientific in character. In practice, faith and science can be distinguished; yet they have much in common. Both combine intuition with cognition. "Even though their role is different in each case, both elements—the intuitive and the cognitive—are present in both religious faith and scientific inquiry. In short, it is not only the case that faith has a cognitive element, it is also the case that rationality has an intuitive element."[64]

Muslim intellectuals find it confusing and, if the situation were not so grave, even humorous to think that Westerners might view Islam as irrational and incapable of scientific thinking.

Munawar Anees, to cite another example, would firmly disagree with Harris' portrait of Islam as a cult of death. Anees denies that the core teachings of Islam support suicide bombings. What Islam teaches is reverence for God and lives of righteousness. "Islam teaches that life is a sacred trust given to human beings by the Creator. Like other Abrahamic faiths, it prohibits suicide as a grave sin. It is forbidden under all circumstances, including war."[65] Anees blames a "highly distorted theology" within some Islamic circles for the promotion of suicide bombing. "It plays upon the young vulnerable psyche that yearns for leading a purposeful life. It systematically misconstrues and misrepresents the Islamic doctrine of salvation."[66] In short, this Muslim's sympathies lie totally with the victims of this brand of religious violence; and he asserts that suicide bombers do not express the heart and center of Islamic teaching. Like the atheists and pluralists, Anees yearns for peace. Yet, his vision of peace derives from his Islamic commitment.

Where in the World is God?

As a theologian considers standing up to reflect out loud about the God affirmed by the Christian faith, he or she must adapt to an environment of competition coming from at least these three directions. The atheists would contend that the burden of proof lies on the shoulders of the theologian to demonstrate that God exists. Ordinarily, theologians proceed on the assumption that there is a divine reality to which the word "God" refers; they seldom stop to provide an image of God which will pass the existence test. Then, it gets worse. Whatever image of God the theologian might defend against the atheists would be disputed by the pluralists, who would contend that this God is but one among many manifestations of the Real which is still more ultimate. And the Muslims will object if the Christian God is portrayed as fully present in the incarnate Son and the gathering Spirit. What's a theologian to do? Let me suggest four recommendations: (1) investigate the truth question; (2) avoid putting God in the equations; (3) affirm what is essential, namely, that the God in whom Christians place their faith is gracious; and (4) practice charity.

Thesis 1: Investigate the Truth Question

When the aggressive atheists complain that religious claims fail to persuade because they lack evidence, the truth of the Christian faith is questioned. Christian claims become subject to analysis. Either they are true, or they are false. Atheists believe they are false.

Christian theologians ought not dodge this challenge. The question of the truth of the Christian claim is internal to theology—that is, theologians need to ask and re-ask: just what is the basis for our belief in God? "The presentation of Christian teaching cannot begin by presupposing the truth," writes Wolfhart Pannenberg. "Theology has to present, test, and if possible confirm the claim. It must treat it, however, as an open question and not decide it in advance."[67] This means that the theologian could conceivably consider each Christian truth claim to be a hypothesis to be confirmed or disconfirmed. A theologian could treat the question of God's existence as a hypothesis too. In this regard, part of the theologian's pursuit is similar to, though not identical with, that of the scientist. The attacks of the aggressive atheists simply remind the theologian of this responsibility to critically review faith's foundations.

The criteria by which these atheists evaluate truth claims might not be acceptable to the theologian, however. As we have seen, what they consider evidence is restricted to the kind of evidence gathered by scientific research on the causal nexus of the material world. They work within a closed naturalism, a view of the world as exhaustibly explainable by natural causes alone. Like a shoe that is two sizes smaller than the foot, scientific naturalism just does not fit a bigger view of reality.

The God rejected in Dawkins' variant of the God-hypothesis is a supernatural personage responsible for creation and providence, an overgrown human being, in effect. In the poetic language of religious symbolism, this God relates to the world and responds personally to us when we pray. Such an overgrown personal being who relates personally to the natural world cannot be found in scientific equations. Could it be that scientific inquiry only asks about impersonal forces? Could it be that scientific inquiry only asks about natural forces? Could it be that a personal and supernatural personal being might not answer the phone if we don't dial the right number?

More importantly, the religious vision rising from within both Islam and Christianity is that our faith is placed not in the symbolic image of a supernatural or overgrown human person; rather, our faith is placed in ultimate reality. That ultimate reality—the really Real, so to speak—transcends both nature and super-nature. God as God transcends even our symbolic images of God. This recognition that the reality of God is beyond our conceptions of God is built right into the self-critical conceptual framework of these two religious traditions. The pluralist position adds nothing that was not already present within the tradition-specific theologies of Christianity and Islam. What this implies is that the evangelical atheists commit a straw religion fallacy, so to speak, by alleging that these two religions teach a primitive supernaturalism with an overgrown human person as their absolute object of devotion. The evangelical atheists have not taken the time to investigate just what Christianity and its sister tradition, Islam, actually teach about God.

Ducking from arrows shot by the evangelical atheists is not enough, however. What remains is for the Christian theologian to return to classic affirmations regarding God understood as the ultimate reality. Because the truth question within religious discourse at first looks different than it does in scientific discourse, the theologian will ask whether the concept of divine ultimacy is coherent and whether it gives authentic expression to what we believe to have been revealed by God in the events surrounding Jesus Christ. The theologian will ask whether the biblical claim that God is the creator makes coherent sense and provides helpful illumination to the creation as pictured by natural science. The theologian presumes consonance, not warfare, between scientific explanation and religious vision.

The theological picture of reality is bigger and includes the scientific picture; even though the reverse is not possible. This does not produce unquestionable truth; but it does provide a more comprehensive and therefore more adequate description of reality. The truth test of Christian claims regarding God is found in the illuminating power of the concept of God for understanding the world which, according to our faith, God has created and promises to redeem. A description of the whole of reality in light of the biblical understanding of the transcendent God provides a more explanatorily adequate understanding than a restrictive naturalism can provide.[68]

More needs to be said here. Even though a comprehensive and coherent picture of reality inclusive of a transcendent divine creator is more adequate than naturalism alone, the Christian theologian is still in the business of proffering a hypothesis that will be either confirmed or disconfirmed by God in the future. Curiously, in the final analysis, the hypothetical structure of knowledge is something theology shares with science.

Even if the Christian concept of God proves itself to illuminate and to expand our understanding, this will not produce unambiguous truth. It will not provide absolute proof that our ideas of God are accurate. For the time being, theological ideas about God must maintain a hypothetical character. Our ideas about God are provisional. They must include recognition of their finite and correctable character, awaiting God's eschatological revelation. "Now we see through a mirror dimly," writes St. Paul. Only eschatologically will we see "face to face" and know God as God has known us (1 Corinthians 13:12).

Thesis 2: Avoid Putting God in the Equations.

If we listen carefully to what the atheists say, there is no place in the world for God. God is missing from the equations; therefore, no God exists. God does not aid us in providing explanations for specific natural phenomena; therefore, no God exists. Should the Christian apologist go back to the equations and add a divine factor? No, I do not recommend this. Rather, I believe the role the concept of God should play in our explanations is a more comprehensive one, a role that draws on both scientific knowledge of the physical world plus knowledge gained from special revelation in Jesus Christ. Because scientific explanations are methodologically reductionistic—that is, by methodological decision scientists look only for proximate physical causes when making an explanation—divine creation and divine providence are excluded from the picture. This is not a problem, as long as the reductionist interpretation remains within the scope of its respective research domain. The theologian, in contrast, offers a more comprehensive explanation based upon distinctively theological resources.

The result should be a picture of the world as the theater of God's gracious presence and care. Theology is an encompassing field, encompassing what we learn from science but not limiting ourselves to only what can be explained scientifically. God's action in the world is more than what science can explain; but what God does is consistent with what science can explain.

> A fire-mist and a planet—
> A crystal and a cell,
> A jelly-fish and a saurian,
> And caves where the cave-men dwell;
> Then a sense of law and beauty
> And a face turned from the clod—
> Some call it Evolution,
> And others call it God.
>
> *William Herbert Carruth, 1859-1924*

With this in mind, let us turn back again to Dawkins. An assumption as big as a horse in a Volkswagen that Dawkins and the new atheists make is that the material world is a closed causal nexus. Physical explanations are the only explanations for any and every phenomenon. There is only one god, the material world, and science is its prophet. But, I ask: suppose the physical world is not merely a closed causal nexus? Are the biological atheists still living in Newton's world of classical physics? The assumption that the causal nexus is closed is just that, an assumption. Perhaps Dawkins should open the Volkswagen door so we can see the horse inside.

Now, what about openness in natural processes, especially evolutionary processes? At the quantum level, for example, the chain of cause and effect is not yet in place, at least according to the Heisenberg school of interpretation. At the quantum level—the most fundamental level of physical activity—no underlying and fully determinate system is governing. Events are contingent, not pre-determined by a fixed set of prior causes. Natural laws can still describe what happens, to be sure; but these are laws of statistical probability. They are not reducible to a set of determining causes. And, because the laws of physics apply everywhere, including biology, we can find openings everywhere, including biology.

Let us take a look at a theological explanation which capitalizes on this observation about openness in the physical realm. Physicist and theologian Robert John Russell locates divine action at the quantum level. He locates divine activity within the realm of statistical probabilities. Because multiple scenarios are statistically possible, whatever action God takes is the actualization of what had previously been possible. God can and does act everywhere in nature, and at no point is a law of nature broken. No interventions. No miracles. Just ubiquitous divine presence. Russell calls this "'NIODA: Non-Interventionist Objective Divine Action'. The idea is that there is an inherent openness in the evolutionary process itself in which God can act. This is not a 'gaps' argument since God is not intervening in evolution; rather God is already immanent in nature as Trinity, acting within the openness that God gifted to the universe in creating it."[69]

Now does this model of divine action, ubiquitous to the material world at the quantum level, constitute a proof for the existence of God? Does it constitute an explanation for natural phenomena that includes God in the equations? No, neither of these. Much more modestly, Russell is trying to provide us with a model of divine action in the natural world that is consistent with science, even if not entailed by science.

As a theologian, Russell has much more to say about reality than he could say as a physicist; but what he says theologically is not inconsistent with what he would say as a physicist. Russell provides us with an example of theological explanation that is consistent with, yet more comprehensive than, scientific explanation. I believe such a method permits us to affirm what is important—that God acts graciously—without restricting ourselves to the suffocating framework within which the atheists require their proofs. It affirms the presence of God while not trying to prove the existence of a personal God within a presumably impersonal and closed causal nexus.

What Russell provides for us is one among many ways in which a Christian theologian can illuminate the world of creatures in light of our understanding of God as the creator and sustainer of this world. God is beyond the equations because God is beyond the world; yet, drawing a picture of the moment by moment dependence of the world upon its divine creator illuminates what surrounds the equations and, indirectly, the equations themselves.

What I advocate here is a two step process. The first step is to withdraw the question of God's existence from making it a scientific hypothesis, at least in the way Dawkins does. The particular concept of God Dawkins hypothesizes about is not the one in which a Christian places his or her faith. Taking this step means the theologian should withdraw into the *two language* model or *independence* model of the relationship between science and religion. Each has its own domain; and each has its own integrity. God is not a scientific hypothesis. Christian theologians can speak of God using religious language on the basis of distinctively theological resources, such as biblical revelation.

The second step is an about face. Once we have re-established the separate languages or separate domains for science and religion, we can then look for new opportunities to build bridges. A good bridge is built from both directions. What Robert John Russell is proposing here is to lay foundations for what could be a bridge between the physical sciences and biblical theology.

Thesis 3: Affirm What is Essential.

Journalists are told by their editors to write the most important point at the beginning of the article. Hit the big one first. If at a later time the editor needs to cut the article to fit the space, the editor snips off the final paragraphs. If the main point had been made at the beginning, it gets printed.

Perhaps we can borrow this principle for theological construction. What is the main point that Christian theologians want to make? Is it that God exists? Not exactly. More important than God's existence is the claim a Christian makes about God's character. The main point of the New Testament witness to Jesus Christ is that the one God—previously the God of Israel but now everybody's God—is gracious. The creator of and redeemer of our universe loves and cares for us and for our world. God hears the cry of those who suffer. God heals the sick. God liberates the oppressed. God raises the dead. God redeems creation with new creation. These are the promises the New Testament has passed on to our generation. What is essential to the Christian witness is this: God is gracious.

Dawkins relishes criticizing the classical Christian proofs for the existence of God. What kind of God appears in these proofs? In Anselm's ontological proof, God is that than which nothing greater can be conceived. In Thomas Aquinas' cosmological proof, God is the first cause of all other causes. These two are Christian answers to the fundamental and shocking question: why is there something and not nothing? The Christian answer is that the God of Israel is responsible for the creation of the world. This does not suffice for Dawkins. "To suggest that the first cause, the great unknown which is responsible for something existing rather than nothing, is a being capable of designing the universe and of talking to a million people simultaneously, is a total abdication of the responsibility to find an explanation. It is a dreadful exhibition of self-indulgent, thought-denying skyhookery."[70] Note that Dawkins cannot actually demonstrate the falsity of the claim that God as primordial cause is responsible for creation; but he believes he can safely deny that God has the kind of personhood that places him in the position of designing the universe and answering millions of prayers.

Just how important is it for a Christian theologian to successfully persuade a non-believer to take on board divine ultimacy in the form of "that than which nothing greater can be conceived" or first cause? It is pretty important, to be sure. But, many non-Christian religions, including Islam, can postulate God as the first principle. And, certainly Dawkins has the right to ask whether this divine first principle can aid in explaining nature's laws. Yet, just any old divine action will not suffice for the Christian claim. What counts for the Christian claim is that the God who acts is gracious, loving, caring, and redeeming. Finding God as one cause among many other natural causes could be interesting, to be sure; but in itself this would not feed the Christian hunger for grace.

In order to bring grace to theological articulation, we would need to rely consciously on the scriptural witness. This would make our faith commitment particularistic. Even though it has universal implications because it deals with the whole of reality; it derives from a historically specific source, namely, God's history with ancient Israel. It takes the form of *confessional universalism*, which I have described elsewhere.[71] One of my former teachers at the University of Chicago, Joseph Sittler, gave voice to this position, even if he did not call it that. "The grace of God whereby 'Christ Jesus has made me my own' establishes the center. But the center is not the circumference; the circumference of the grace which is redemption is not smaller than that theatre of life and awareness which is the creation."[72] Here is the key: the center is not the circumference; yet, the center enjoins us to appreciate all that we do not understand lying between the center and the circumference. I confess as a Christian that God's grace expressed in Jesus Christ extends to all of creation, and this includes believers and nonbelievers of every religious tradition.

This theological articulation will find some continuity along with some discontinuity with what a Muslim might want to affirm. Continuity because Muslims also believe God is "compassionate." Discontinuity because of the involvement Christians believe God has in the beloved world.

What about pluralism? This theological focus on divine grace would resist subordination of the Trinity to a higher "Real" in the conceptual framework of the religious pluralist. The Christian claim that God is gracious is either right or wrong. It is not a brick to be built into someone else's wall. What is at stake here is not the particularist nature of the Christian claim, but rather its truth value for understanding the whole of reality.

Thesis 4: Practice Charity.

Affirming the presence of a gracious God leads to a life of love, a life of charity. Jesus is unambiguous. [NRS] Luke 10:27: "You shall love the Lord your God with all your heart, and with all your soul, and with all your strength, and with all your mind; and your neighbor as yourself." That we should love the other as other rather than as a means to further our own ends becomes clear when Jesus tells us to love even our enemies. [NRS] Matthew 5:44: "Love your enemies and pray for those who persecute you," The impact of faith in a God of love is a life of love.

Curiously, this has epistemological implications. What Christians have learned through our long history is this: the only way to come to know the God of Jesus is to live the life of a follower of Jesus. Discipleship is what leads to knowledge of God. God cannot be found in the equations; but God can reveal the Godself to the disciple, to the follower of Jesus. The life of love becomes revelatory.

In the next lecture we will explore how the Theology of the Cross might illuminate the suffering within nature throughout its immense evolutionary history. An aspect of the Theology of the Cross might be relevant here. It is difficult if not impossible to see God as the all-powerful and eternal deity when looking at the focal revelation, namely, the suffering of Jesus on the cross. God's eternal life is hidden behind a mask of death. God's healing grace is hidden behind a mask of suffering. Martin Luther puts it this way: "The manifest and visible things of God are placed in opposition to the invisible, namely, his human nature, weakness, foolishness…in the humility and shame of the cross."[73] To understand God, says Luther, we must look at the cross and recognize that we do not understand God. What we add to this epistemological paradox is the role of discipleship. To walk the walk of Jesus places us in a position to gain the insight, to be visited by the knowledge that there is a God, and this God is gracious. It is the cross-walk, so to speak, that makes knowledge of our gracious and loving God possible.

Although virtually all Christians agree on the priority of discipleship and the life of love, some disagreement has arisen regarding just how to practice charitable love. Does Jesus' act of self-giving love which incarnates God's grace constitute a unique divine capacity? Or, do we, the followers of Jesus, have the same capacity to go to the same extreme Jesus did? Is it possible for us to realize in our own lives in this world the very disinterested (*agape*) love by which God has loved us?[74] Or, because of the inevitable and inescapable conflicts in our social life, should we engage in a compromising morality? Should we embrace full pacifism and practice total nonviolence; or, should we construct a theory of the just war to warrant occasional violent actions on behalf of justice and peace? Regardless of which side a Christian elects, both are committed to loving God and neighbor.

As we watch the competition for survival within the cultural niche traditionally held by classical religion, we note how the two focal concerns seem to be knowledge of God and peaceful co-existence with someone who is other. Although Christian theologians should feel responsible to address the epistemological concerns raised by atheism, pluralism, and Islam, the indispensable role played by discipleship in knowing God needs to find its rightful place. In an era where a violent world is scrambling painfully to find a road to peace, perhaps the road of discipleship which begins with a commitment to a loving peace might lead to a more illuminative understanding of God.

Notes

1. Gary Wolf, "The Church of the Non-Believers, *Wired* (November 2006) 182-193. Not every atheist can be described accurately as militant, aggressive, or evangelical. Alan G. Padgett describes the atheists he knows as uninterested in religion while still respecting religion. "On Atheism, Pluralism, and Science: A Response to Ted Peters," *Dialog,* 46:4 (Winter 2007) 393-395. Perhaps atheism could have its militant and passive sects just as religion can. The subject of this chapter is the new wave of extremist atheists who announce that they are launching an attack against religion.
2. Peter Atkins, "Atheism and Science," in Philip Clayton and Zachary Simpson, editors, *The Oxford Handbook of Religion and Science* (Oxford and New York: Oxford University Press, 2006) 136. In my own attempt to classify the variety of ways in which science and religion relate, the most belligerent is *scientism*, a warfare model in which science attempts to defeat religion entirely and replace it. See: Ted Peters, *Science, Theology, and Ethics* (Aldershot UK: Ashgate, 2003) 16-17. Danniel C. Dennett provides an example. "If we persist with the [religious] myths, if we dare not run them in for scientifically sound replacements—which are available--our flying days may be numbered. The truth really will set you free." *Freedom Evolves* (New York: Viking, 2003) 22.
3. Van A. Harvey, "Agnosticism and Atheism, Definitional Issues," in *The New Encyclopedia of Unbelief,* edited by Tom Flynn (Amherst NY: Prometheus Press, 2007) 35.
4. Paul Kurtz, *The Transcendental Temptation: A Critique of Religion and the Paranormal* (Buffalo, NY: Prometheus Books, 1986) 316.
5. Definitions of "atheism" can be tricky. Does atheism entail an active denial of God's existence or only a passive non-affirmation of same? On the one hand, George H. Smith allows the passive non-belief to be considered inclusive. "*Atheism, in its basic form, is not a belief: it is the absence of belief.* An atheist is not primarily a person who *believes* that a god does *not* exist; rather he does *not believe* in the existence of a god." *Atheism: The Case Against God* (Buffalo NY: Prometheus Books, 1979) 7, italics in original. On the other hand, Smith takes up the cause of "critical atheism" which actively asserts that "belief in a god is entirely unsupported and, further, that there are many reasons for not believing in a god." Ibid., 18.
6. Simon Conway Morris describes Richard Dawkins as "arguably England's most pious atheist." *Life's Solution: Inevitable Humans in a Lonely Universe* (Cambridge: Cambridge University Press, 2003) 315.
7. Richard Dawkins, *The Selfish Gene* (Oxford and New York: Oxford University Press, 1979, 1989).

8. Richard Dawkins, *The God Delusion* (Boston and New York: Houghton Mifflin Company, 2006) 31, Dawkins' italics. See the official Dawkins website: http://richarddawkins.net/home. Dawkins has sparked support among like minded scientists, such as Nobel Prize winning biologist, David Baltimore. "I am glad Dawkins took the time to write *The God Delusion* at this moment in history. In the United States, there is an increasingly pervasive assumption that Christianity is our state religion. In fact, the tolerance of other religions that was so much a part of American politics, at least in the post-World War II era, is giving way to an increasing focus on Christianity as the only true belief." See his "A Defense of Atheism" in *American Scientist* (January—February 2007): http://www.americanscientist.org/template/AssetDetail/assetid/54417

9. Dawkins, *The God Delusion*, 156. Wesley J. Wildman contrasts two models of God extent in the current dialogue between science and religion. The first model treats God as a *determinate entity,* holding "that God is an existent entity with determinate features including intentions, plans, and capacities to act." It would appear that the God Dawkins and his atheist fellow travelers reject is this determinate entity. This is the pre-modern God of supranaturalism. Wildman goes on to identify a rival model, *Ground-of-Being* theism, which "challenges the very vocabulary of divine existence or non-existence." Because God is being-itself, according to this second model, there is no personal entity or determinate being along side the rest of us beings. Such a God would be invisible to a Dawkins style analysis. "Ground-of-Being Theologies," in *The Oxford Handbook of Religion and Science,* 612.

10. Not everyone who examines evolution concludes that atheism follows. The famous atheistic philosopher, Anthony Flew, at age 81, drew exactly the opposite conclusion, so it seems. Investigation into the evolution of DNA has "shown by the almost unbelievable complexity of the arrangements which are needed to produce [life], that intelligence must have been involved." Cited by Richard N. Ostling, "DNA Draws Atheist to God—Sort of," *Chicago Sun-Times* (10 December, 2004). The emergence of life supports a rational belief in God. Now, the God of Flew looks a bit more deistic than theistic—that is, God orders nature but does not get involved. This leads William Schweiker to caution us about "how little Professor Flew is actually saying. Religiously and theologically considered, it is not at all clear that atheism is actually in retreat. It may have merely assumed another guise." "The Varieties and Revisions of Atheism," *Zygon* 40:2 (June 2005) 271.

11. George V. Coyne, S.J., "The Evolution of Intelligent Life on Earth and Possibly Elsewhere: Reflections from a Religious Tradition," in *Many Worlds: The New Universe, Extraterrestrial Life and the Theological Implications,* edited by Steven Dick (Philadelphia and London: Templeton Foundation Press, 2000) 186.

12. Michael Shermer, *How We Believe: The Search for God in an Age of Science* (New York: W.H. Freeman and Col, 2000) 236. Shermer would not agree completely with Dawkins. When Dawkins blames religion for suicide bombers and other recent violent incidents, Shermer comments. "In my opinion, many of these events—and others often attributed solely to religion by atheists—were less religiously motivated than politically driven, or at the very least involved religion in the service of political hegemony." "Arguing for Atheism," *Science,* 315:5811 (26 January 2007) 463.

13. Nancey Murphy, "Is Altruism Good? Evolution, Ethics, and the Hunger for Theology," *Zygon* 41:4:985-994 (December 2006) 993.
14. Marilynne Robinson, "Hysterical Scientism: The Ecstasy of Richard Dawkins, *Harper's Magazine* (November 2006) 86.
15. Michael Ruse, "Darwinism: Foe or Friend? *The Evolution of Rationality: Interdisciplinary Essays in Honor of J. Wentzel van Huyssettn,* edited by F. LeRon Shults (Grand Rapids: William B. Eerdmans, 2006) 238.
16. John B. Cobb, Jr., *Christ in a Pluralistic Age* (Louisville: Westminster John Knox Press, 1975) 58.
17. Paul F. Knitter, *Theologies of Religions* (Maryknoll NY: Orbis, 2002) 110. Menno Simons would not likely be considered an ally by religious pluralists. With his emphasis on purifying the Christian community and on exclusive communion, he might be dubbed an "exclusivist." He wrote, "Go ye into all the world, and preach the gospel to every creature; he that believeth and is baptized shall be saved, but he that believeth not, shall be damned." *Dat Fundament des Chrystelycken leers,* or "The Foundation of Christian Doctrine" (1539).
18. Langdon Gilkey, *Through the Tempest: Theological Voyages in a Pluralistic Culture* (Minneapolis: Fortress Press, 1991) 181.
19. Ibid., 153. Peter C. Hodgson asserts that Liberal Theology should incorporate into the Christian faith "a genuine religious pluralism that accepts a diversity of ways of salvation, declines to rank them in a graded hierarchy, and encourages dialogue between them as equals." *Liberal Theology: A Radical Vision* (Minneapolis: Fortress Press, 2007) 87. Hodgson's position teeters between pluralism and inclusivism, because it is a distinctively Christian interpretation of God's trinitarian Spirit at work in the world's religions. Ibid., 90.
20. John Hick, *An Interpretation of Religion: Human Responses to the Transcendent* (New Haven and London: Yale University Press, 1989) 240.
21. Ibid., 242.
22. Herbert Spencer, *First Principles* (New York: D. Appleton and Company, 1897) 45.
23. David Ray Griffin, "Religious Pluralism: Generic, Identist, and Deep," in *Deep Religious Pluralism*, ed. by David Ray Griffin (Louisville: Westminster John Knox Press, 2005) 3. Griffin also distinguishes between *identist pluralism* such as we find in the work of John Hick that declares all perspectival religions to be oriented to the same transcendent Real; *differential pluralism* such as we find in the work of S. Mark Heim that understands different religions as promoting different ultimates or ends; and *deep pluralism* such as one might find in Whtieheadian process theologians, specifically John Cobb, which recognizes that religious diversity involves real differences, that both shared truths and irresolvable differences reside in religions other than one's own.
24. Ibid., 4.
25. Gordon D. Kaufman, *God, Mystery, Diversity* (Minneapolis: Fortress Press, 1996) 118-119. Although Kaufman is not a disciple of John Hick on all counts, he grants that he is sympathetic. Ibid. 187.
26. Ibid., 191.
27. Ibid., 202. Kaufman also attempts to revise his understanding of God in light

of evolutionary science and ecological ethics. Rejecting as does Dawkins the idea of God as a person, Kaufman describes God as *serendipitous creativity*. "If God is understood as the creativity manifest throughout the cosmos—instead of as a kind of cosmic person—and we humans are understood as deeply embedded in, and basically sustained by, this creative activity in and through the web of life on planet Earth, we will be strongly encouraged to develop attitudes and to participate in activities that fit properly into this web of living creativity, all members of which are neighbors that we should love and respect." *In the Beginning...Creativity* (Minneapolis: Fortress Press, 2004) 48. This reconstruction of the image of God has implications for anthropology and ecclesiology. "We humans are indissolubly a part of the created order. In this picture the too-easy human-centeredness, and Christian-centeredness, of traditional Christian thinking is thoroughly undercut." Ibid., 50.

28. Sam Harris, *Letter to a Christian Nation* (New York: Alfred A. Knopf, 2006) 80.
29. Kaufman, *God, Mystery, Diversity*, 202.
30. Diana Eck, "Prospects for Pluralism: Voice and Vision in the Study of Religion," *Journal of the American Academy of Religion,* 75:4 (December 2007) 745. See: *Encountering God: A Spiritual Journey from Bozeman to Banaras* (Boston: Beacon, 1993). See; Kristin Johnston Largen, "On Pluralism, Comparative Theology & Tariq Ramadan: A Response to Ted Peters," *Dialog,* 46:4 (Winter 2007) 408-412.
31. Paul O. Ingram, *Wrestling with God* (Eugene OR: Cascade Books, 2006) 9.
32. Seyyed Hossein Nasr, "Islam and Science," in *The Oxford Handbook of Religion and Science,* 76.
33. Badru D. Kateregga and David W. Shenk, *A Muslim and a Christian in Dialogue* (Scottdale PA and Waterloo, Ontario: Herald Press, 1997) 28.
34. Mark N. Swanson, "The Trinity in Christian-Muslim Conversation," *Dialog* 44:3 (Fall 2005) 257.
35. Al-Ghazali, "The Elegant Refutation," in *Judaism, Christianity, and Islam: The Classical Texts and Their Interpretation,* edited by F.E. Peters (Princeton NJ: Princeton University Press, 1990) 1087.
36. Kenneth Cragg, *The Call of the Minaret* (New York: Oxford University Press, 1964) 308.
37. "Declaration on the Relationship of the Church to Non-Christian Religions (*Nostra Aetate*) 3.
38. Kateregga and Shenk, *Dialogue*, 34-35.
39. Alain Besançon, "What Kind of Religion is Islam? *Commentary* (May 2004) 45.
40. Ibid., 121.
41. Ibid., 120.
42. Swanson, "The Trinity," 261.
43. *A Common Word between Us and You,* http://www.acommonword.com/ .
44. Abdulaziz Sachedina, *The Role of Islam in the Public Square: Guidance or Governance?* (Leiden: Amsterdam University Press, 2006) 5.
45. Ibid., 14-15.
46. Susan Blackmore, *The Meme Machine* (Oxford and New York: Oxford University Press, 1999) 199. Research scientists are showing an interest in the possible connection

between religion and violence. One hypothesis is that "if violence is presented as the authoritative voice of God, it can increase the possibility of more violence." "Scriptural Violence Can Foster Aggression," *Nature* 446: 7132 (8 March 2007) 114-115. The question is whether religion is the "cause" of violence or if something else is the cause while religion exacerbates violence. New Religious Movements scholar Mark Juergensmeyer is cited saying, "Religion is not the problem; but it can make a secular problem worse." Ibid.

47. Christopher Hitchens, *God is Not Great: How Religion Poisons Everything* (New York and Boston: Twelve, 2007) 4.
48. Ibid., 46-47.
49. Ibid., 12.
50. Sam Harris, *The End of Faith: Religion, Terror, and the Future of Reason* (New York and London: W.W. Norton, 2004) 236.
51. Ibid. 131.
52. Harris, *Letter to a Christian Nation,* 85, author's italics.
53. Harris, *End of Faith.*, 123.
54. Ibid., 110.
55. Ibid., 129.
56. Ibid., 131.
57. Dawkins, *God Delusion*, 306.
58. Ibid., 308. Alister McGrath observes that Dawkins engages in "absolute dichotomist thinking, that is typical of fundamentalisms, whether religious or antireligious. Where some divide the world into the saved and the damned, Dawkins divides into those who follow the ways of rationalism and superstition." "Dawkins, God, and the Scientific Enterprise" in *Intelligent Design: William A. Dembski and Michael Ruse in Dialogue,* edited by Robert B. Stewart (Minneapolis: Fortress Press, 2007) 103. See also by Alister E. McGrath and Joanna Collicutt McGrath, *The Dawkins Delusion? Atheist Fundamentalism and the Denial of the Divine* (Downers Grove IL: InterVarsity 2007).
59. Harris, *End of Faith*, 22-23. Bishop John Shelby Spong recently acknowledged some value to the criticisms of "Richard Dawkins and Sam Harris." Yet, he went on to say, "Their biggest problem is not their criticism, which I find quite accurate, but that the Christianity they reject is a very poor representation of what Christianity was meant to be. It is because they know no other Christianity than this popular expression, they believe that atheism is the only viable alternative to the Christianity they have known and rejected. They have never explored the essence of Christianity because that essence lives in such tiny and hidden places." "Bishop Spong Q&A On When People Talk About God," qna@johshelbyspong.com, 1/17/2007.
60. Tom Pyszcznski, Sheldon Solomon, and Jeff Greenberg, *In the Wake of 9/11: The Psychology of Terror* (Washington DC: American Psychological Association, 2003) 148.
61. Harris, *End of Faith*, 79.
62. Dawkins, *God Delusion,* 278.
63. Robinson, "Hysterical Scientism," 84.
64. Basit Bilal Koshul, "From 'Religion and Science' to '*Kalam* and Science'," *Dialog,*

46:3 (Fall 2007) 244.

65. Munawar A. Anees, "Salvation and Suicide: What Does Islamic Theology Say?" *Dialog* 45:3 (Fall 2006) 277.

66. Ibid., 278.

67. Wolfhart Pannenberg, *Systematic Theology,* tr. by Geoffrey W. Bromily, 3 Volumes (Grand Rapids MI: Wm. B. Eerdmans, 1991-1998) 1:50.

68. The method of testing Christian theological claims centers on what I call "explanatory adequacy." An illuminative concept of God and God's relationship to the world should provide increased explanatory power, I contend. This methodological understanding is described in chapter two of Ted Peters, *GOD—The World's Future* (Minneapolis: Fortress Press, 2nd ed., 2000).

69. Robert John Russell, *Cosmology, Evolution, and Resurrection Hope: Theology and Science in Creative Mutual Interaction*, edited by Carl S. Helrich on behalf of the Fifth Annual Goshen Conference on Religion and Science (Kirchener, Ontario: Pandora Press and Adelaide, South Australia: ATF Press, 2006) 28. See: *God's Action in Nature's World: Essays in Honor of Robert John Russell,* edited by Ted Peters and Nathan Hallanger (Aldershot UK: Ashgate, 2006) 9-12; 57-58; 99-104.

70. Dawkins, *God Delusion*, 155.

71. Peters, *GOD—The World's Future,* Chapter 11. Pannenberg embraces confessional universalism when raising the truth question. "*My* truth cannot be mine alone. If I cannot in principle declare it to be truth for all…then it pitilessly ceases to be truth for me also." *Systematic Theology*, 1:51.

72. Joseph Sittler, *Essays on Nature and Grace* (Minneapolis: Fortress Press, 1972) 35.

73. Martin Luther, *Luther's Works*, American Edition, Vols. 1-30, edited by Jaroslav Pelikan (St. Louis: Concordia Publishing Company, 1955-1967); Vols. 31-55, edited by Helmut T. Lehmann (Minneapolis: Fortress Press, 1955-1986) 31:53.

74. "There has been disagreement among Christians from that time to the present over whether Jesus' example of selfless love (agape) was meant to be followed to similar extremes by other members of the Christian community." Mark Juergensmeyer, "Nonviolence," in *Encyclopedia of Religion,* 2nd edition, edited by Lindsay Jones (14 Volumes: New York: MacMillan, Gale, 2005). 10:6647.

Lecture Two

Evolving Evil and the Theology of the Cross

Where in the world is God? One of the most difficult matrices of questions within which to find God are those dealing with evolution. Do we find God blessing the victors in the relentless struggle for survival-of-the-fittest? Does God crown the lion with a mane after downing the gazelle? Does God crown the species which adapted with a period of dominance, until it is trodden into extinction by its replacement species? Or, does God identify with the weak, the losers, the unfit? Does God share in the fear of the gazelle during the death chase? Does God mourn the loss of species after species as they fossilize under the mud of geological history?

It is the question of purpose in nature that keeps the theologian up late at night. It is the bushel of questions surrounding loss, violence, disease, suffering, death, and extinction that put the bite on doctrines such as creation and providence. It is the theodicy question once again, the question of finding a gracious God within a suffering creation.

The question of evolving evil cannot easily be heard these days, given the din of horn blowing by the Darwinists and drum banging by the anti-Darwinists. What blasts in our ears is the noise of controversy over whether the Darwinian model of evolution should receive exclusive attention in science classrooms. The biblical creationists ask: how can Darwinism be defeated on the basis of the authority of the book of Genesis? The scientific creationists ask: how can Darwin's concept of speciation be refuted on the basis of geological evidence? The Intelligent Design advocates ask: how can the Darwinian reliance on natural selection be overturned in favor of leaps in design by a transcendent designer?

Curiously, I want to say: none of these are the questions I wish to address here. Rather, I would like to address a different kind of question: *given the long history of life's development according to the Darwinian conceptual model, how can we hold together our faith in a God of grace with what we know about predation, parasitism, violence, suffering, death, and extinction?* Just how can we reconcile this picture of nature with our picture of God as almighty creator and loving provider? This is the theodicy question as we ask it within the framework of evolving evil.

On the one hand, we must accept Theodosius Dobzhansky's aphorism, "In biology nothing makes sense except in the light of evolution."[1] On the other hand, nothing in Christian theology makes sense except in the light of the cross and resurrection. How might these be brought together?

The Darwinian Theodicy Problem

Most of Christian theology has made its peace with Darwin. In fact, the evolutionary worldview has supplemented if not merged with the Christian worldview. Ann Milliken Pederson and Philip Hefner recommend this with a touch of eloquence: "The Darwinian narrative may take the form of genetic influence—omnipresent now in medicine; or neuroscience and cognitive science—our brain and our mind, are woven on a Darwinian loom; or evolutionary psychology—our evolutionary history has bequeathed to us behaviors and even traits and emotions that form the foundation for how we think and feel and build our lives today. This has become our narrative."[2] Now that the Darwinian model of evolution is becoming our religious narrative, we can see that the overall plot is one of advance, perhaps even of progress. Yet, is there a sub-plot as well, a contrapuntal narrative? Might a most resistant form of the theodicy problem be hiding in this narrative?

Darwin's theory of evolution relies upon three complementary principles: variation in inheritance, natural selection, and common descent. Our focus here is on the mechanism of natural selection, according to which a new species will evolve out of a previous one. Slight random differences in biological heredity will dispose some individuals more than others to withstand the threats and challenges of the environment. Those who survive to the age of reproduction will pass on their heritable traits. The genomes of those who die before they can make babies will disappear into the oblivion of nature's history. The genes that survive we call "adapted." They are the fit. They have been selected by nature to advance forward.

Some inherited variations—what today we call genes—get selected for preservation. Others go extinct. Sociobiologists and Evolutionary Psychologists would like us to believe that it is the gene that drives evolutionary history. The gene—or, better, the DNA sequence—is selfish, so to speak. The gene's strong desire to replicate itself in organism after organism in perpetuity is what provides us with our inheritance. What Darwin noticed was randomness in this inheritance. Environmental forces would then select from among the inherited characteristics, from among the genetic variations. In *Origin of Species,* Charles Darwin put it this way: "If variations useful to any organic being ever do occur, assuredly individuals thus characterized will have the best chance of being preserved in the struggle for life; and from the strong principle of inheritance, these will tend to produce offspring similarly characterized. This principle of preservation, or the survival of the fittest, I have called Natural Selection."[3]

Darwin's theory of natural selection seems to shine a revelatory light on the long trail life has traversed over deep time. He could wax eloquently about the complex beauty of nature as well as the advance of higher intelligence. "Thus, from the war of nature, from famine and death, the most exalted object which we are capable of conceiving, namely the production of the higher animals, directly follows. There is grandeur in this view of life...from so simple a beginning endless forms most beautiful and most wonderful have been, and are being evolved."[4] If the evolutionary story becomes our narrative, there will be grandeur in it.

Yet, a shadow follows this trail of light. New life depends on the death of the old. New species require the extinction of their predecessors and even their progenitors. The grandeur of evolved life seems to require the wanton sacrifice of discarded living creatures. One thing Charles Darwin himself noticed is that nature produces far more offspring than can survive to reproductive age. Nature is profligate, almost planning for widespread death to serve the larger purpose of selection. Because more individuals are produced than can possibly survive, there must in every case be a struggle for existence, either one individual with another of the same species, or with the individuals of distinct species, or with the physical conditions of life. This means that early death is scheduled for large numbers of those creatures who get born. Nature has no intention to draw each individual life toward fulfillment, toward actualizing its inborn potential. If suffering befalls the less than fully fit, nature sheds no tears. Nature is pitiless.[5]

The contrapuntal sub-plot within the larger narrative is what Stephen Jay Gould described as the "messy, relentless slaughter" of evolution.[6] "The amount of suffering per year in the natural world is beyond all decent contemplation," writes philosopher of science Michael Ruse. "During the minute it takes me to compose this sentence, thousands of animals are being eaten alive; others are running for their lives, whimpering with fear; others are being slowly devoured from within by rasping parasites; thousands of all kinds are dying of starvation, thirst, and disease. It must be so."[7]

The demand of the predator to kill and devour its prey is a ubiquitous part of this universal struggle. Reproducing requires living. Living requires eating. Eating requires killing. And the form that killing takes seems cruel and harsh and unnecessary. This observation haunts the theologian with the theodicy question: would a God of grace build a machine that unceremoniously chews up and spits out its sentient children? Francisco J. Ayala answers: no. "The human jaw is poorly designed, lions devour their prey, malaria parasites kill millions of humans every year and make 500 million sick. I do not attribute all this misery, cruelty, and destruction to the specific design of the Creator.... I rather see it as a consequence of the clumsy ways of the evolutionary process."[8] One way to win in the wrestling match with evil and suffering is to attribute it to the clumsy evolutionary process rather than to God the creator. Ayala suggests that this is Darwin's gift to theology.

Darwin himself wrestled with this very same theodicy problem: how does one perceive divine grace in a creation where so much unnecessary suffering is the order of the day, every day? In a letter, Darwin writes, "I had no intention to write atheistically. But I own that I cannot see as plainly as others do, and as I should wish to do, evidence of design and beneficence on all sides of us. There seems to me too much misery in the world. I cannot persuade myself that a beneficent and omnipotent God would have designedly created the Ichneumonidae [insects whose larvae are usually internal parasites of other insect larvae] with the express intention of their feeding within the living bodies of caterpillars, or that a cat should play with mice. Not believing this, I see no necessity in the belief that the eye was expressly designed."[9] The violence of predation combined with massive extinctions led Darwin to use the term "waste" to describe nature's debris. Could waste on such a scale be reconciled with the love of God? Not according to Darwin. Better to attribute it to natural processes than to divine intention.

When Richard Dawkins confronts this issue, he gives no thought to reconciling nature's cruelty or waste with divine grace. He offers little sympathy to Darwin in his struggle. Why? Because we should not ask nature to be more than what it is, namely, pitiless. Darwin's "reference to the Ichneumonidae was aphoristic. The macabre habits to which he referred and are shared by their cousins the digger wasps....A female digger wasp not only lays her egg in a caterpillar (or grasshopper or bee) so that her larva can feed on it but...she carefully guides her sting into each ganglion of the prey's central nervous system, so as to paralyze it *but not kill it*. This way, the meat keeps fresh....This sounds savagely cruel but...nature is not cruel, only pitilessly indifferent. This is one of the hardest lessons for humans to learn."[10]

Yes, indeed, Dr. Dawkins, this is one of the hardest lessons for humans to learn! It amounts to one of the most forceful challenges to belief in a loving and gracious God. What the person of faith confronts here is a form of the truth question. These days we do not search for apodictic truth; but we can ask for a better rather than a worse explanation. Let us ask, then: which explanation is the better one: the atheistic or the theological? The atheistic explanation would simply accept that nature is pitiless and without meaning. The theological explanation would accept that nature is pitiless but demand that it have meaning. Both need to deal honestly with the fact that new species emerge from the extinction of the old and that all creatures, including ourselves, can live only through killing. Just where does a God of grace or love or care fit into this picture of the world?

Just What Is The Problem With Suffering And Evil?

As we drill beneath the layers of our understanding of suffering to ask whether or not it is evil, we need to acknowledge the complex and indispensable role death plays. Some living thing needs to die for others to live. Some living thing needs to be sacrificed if we are going to eat. The only non-living thing we human beings eat is salt, which comes from rocks. Everything else is a plant or an animal. Life feeds off life. This is the natural world we have inherited.

Many Christian families say table grace. These table prayers thank God for "daily bread."

> Come Lord Jesus
> Be our guest.
> Let these gifts
> To us be blest.
> Amen

America's annual Thanksgiving Day is a day of national gratitude for the bounty the farm land, the pastures, and the forests have provided for our sustenance. We hardly ever remind ourselves that our life is provided for by the death of so many living plants and animals. Christians right along with other religiously sensitive people express gratitude for those beings who died so that we might be nourished. One can imagine gratitude for daily bread from another point of view within the natural realm.

> There once was a lady from Hyde,
> Who was carried away by the tide.
> A man-eating shark
> Was heard to remark,
> "I knew the Lord would provide."

In addition to the death of one so that another might live, evolutionary history is replete with the extinction of one species to make room for a new one to take its place. If one believes in progress, extinction is a form of sacrifice that makes possible nature's advance. Without prior extinctions of many potential predators and predecessors, *homo sapiens* might not have evolved.

So, just what is the focus of this version of the theodicy problem? Christopher Southgate asks: is it pain? No, he answers. The sensitivity to pain we and other higher animals have is necessary for a richer experience. Is it death? No, he answers. Death is a thermodynamic necessity. Further, we cannot say death is evil if it follows a fulfilled life. Rather, says Southgate, the heart of the problem is that so many creatures are cut down mercilessly before they can experience the richness of a fulfilled life. Think of the newly born impala torn apart and devoured by the hyena. We cannot count the sufferers of predation and parasitism, including organisms for which life seems to contain no fullness, no expression of what it is to reach the potential inherent in being a creature. Indeed, nature's profligacy in producing far more babies than we could expect to survive means that snuffing out individuals long before fulfillment is the mass victimage perpetrated by evolution.[11]

The Temporal Sequence Conflict

Are our human propensities to sin part of our genetic inheritance? Did the first Adam and Eve inherit an already established biological propensity to fight for survival, to kill competitors, real and imagined? Creationists would say "no"; whereas theistic evolutionists would cautiously say "yes." For the creationists, what we know as predation and death entered an already good creation with the fall of the human race into sin. The now late Henry M. Morris, former president of the Institute for Creation Research, treats the sequence of events spelled out in the early chapters of Genesis as past history. In the beginning, "there could have been nothing that was not good in all creation: no struggle for existence, no disease, no pollution, no physical calamities (earthquakes, floods, etc.), no imbalance or lack of harmony, no disorder, no sin and, above all, no death!" Yet, he observes, "fossils, of course speak of death—often of violent and sudden death." How could this be explained? "Since death only 'entered into the world' when sin came in through man (Romans 5:12), and since the whole creation was very good before man sinned,...the fossil record now found in the sedimentary rocks of the earth's crust could only have been formed sometime after man sinned."[12]

This uncovers what we might call this the *temporal sequence conflict* between the creationist account and the Darwinian account. According to the creationist account, during a historical era in the past our earth enjoyed a state of perfection, a Garden of Eden. Theists who incorporate the Darwinian story of evolution, however, can find no time in earth's historical past when such a Garden of Eden could have existed. Yet, theistic evolutionists similarly affirm that God created the human race; and, further, the history of evolution is the means by which God did and does this creating. The particular version of theistic evolution proposed in this book locates the

Garden of Eden in the New Jerusalem (Revelation 21-22)—that is, the state of perfection is God's promise, not earth's history. Whereas a creationist believes Genesis 1:1-2:4a tells of a historical event that was completed in the past; the theistic evolutionist believes we today are still living in the world of Genesis 1 and looking forward to a future Sabbath when God will say, "behold, it is very good."[13]

The temporal sequence conflict is severe enough for creationists to flatly reject the Darwinian model that includes common descent for all living beings, including the human race. We humans are the result of a special act of creation on God's part, say the creationists. We were originally placed in an Edenic world of harmony—that is, the writer and reader of this book belong to the species that introduced the natural world to disharmony. Evolutionary theists, in contrast, accept the Darwinian notion of common descent complete with continuity between today's human race and yesterday's predatory ancestors. All of creation exhibits the signs of so-called fallenness; and all of creation will benefit from the divine promise of an eschatological new creation. What we are pursuing now is the question: just how much of nature's disharmony have we inherited and continue to pass on? Can we speak of our evolutionary inheritance as original sin? This question is posed theologically from within the Darwinian model of common descent.

The Human Contribution to Evil and Suffering

If we *homo sapiens* share a common ancestor six million years ago with higher primates—such as chimpanzees, gorillas, bonobos, and orangutans—and if these species are capable of deceit, rape, murder, and even genocide, should we be surprised if our own species is similarly capable? "Human savagery is not unique. It is shared by other party-gang species.... Our ape ancestors have passed to us a legacy, defined by the power of natural selection and written in the molecular chemistry of DNA."[14]

Not everyone would rely completely on a doctrine of genetic determinism here. Despite sharing more than 98% of our genes with chimpanzees, we humans are quite distinguishable from our primate relatives. Jonathan Marks is not inclined to dub us victims of our chimp genes. "We're the one's walking upright, speaking, weeping, laughing, praising, insulting; we're the ones with erotic sexual foreplay and sex games, the ones who fall in love, who cook our food, who decorate ourselves for public display. So different from chimpanzees, and yet all the while genetically so similar to them."[15] Despite these differences, theologians still need to explore the possible significance of genetically inherited propensities to violence.

If the human inclination toward violent behavior comes to us through our genes, might we identify our inheritance as a sort of original sin? At least, inherited sin? "The roots of all evil can be seen in natural selection, and are expressed (along with much that is good) in human nature," writes sociobiologist Robert Wright. "The enemy of justice and decency does indeed lie in our genes."[16]

If the selfish gene theory holds, might we have here an explanation for genocide? Might it be the case that members of families and clans and races identify with one another because of genetic proximity? Because they share a larger proportion of their DNA with this in-group? Might we unconsciously decide that other groups who are more genetically distant are competing with us for survival? Might we then devise a self-justification to go to war and wipe them out? Would we be able to say following a successful genocide: my genes made me do it? Theologian Patricia Williams leaps to the logical conclusion. "Under both group selection and kin selection, racism and genocide are natural. Only within groups is charity likely to flourish."[17] So persuaded is Williams that she can say, "because sin remains central, science and Christianity can be united."[18]

Williams relies on sociobiology, which many doubt to be a credible science. Still, the issue deserves attention, with or without sociobiology and its concept of the selfish gene. "While the roots of genocide and mass killing cannot be attributed solely to the deep traces of design left in the mind by natural selection," comments James Waller, "people can no longer dismiss as an unsupportable theological or philosophical assumption that human nature has a dark side. Evil deeds are at least partially grounded in human nature. An impulse to do evil is not *the* defining characteristic of human nature, but the impulse is certainly within human capacity."[19] Is it reasonable to say that the impulse we human beings have to perform evil acts and inflict suffering on others derives, at least in part, from our evolutionary inheritance?

Waller would certainly say, yes, with regard to our strong inclination to divide the human race into in-groups and out-groups, into friends and enemies. "We have an evolved capacity to see our group as superior to all others and even to be reluctant to recognize members of other groups as deserving of equal respect. Some even suggest that our tendency to divide the world into 'us' and 'them' is one of the few true human universals."[20] It is this habit of dividing others into friends and enemies that leads us to justify going to war, and even on rare occasions, genocide.

Sin is a human act that produces evil. Evil is an event that produces suffering. The problem with sin and evil is that someone eventually suffers. Has our evolved inheritance led us to the point where we are genetically disposed to inflict suffering? Is suffering so built into our evolutionary biology that no alternative form of living is conceivable? Should we offer thanksgiving to natural selection for making us this way?

Theistic Evolution and the Root of Evil

Might a theologian want to absorb into his or her religious vision this evolutionary picture of the human race? Could the theory of evolution influence Christian anthropology? Theistic evolutionists would answer, yes. "Theologians should acknowledge that it is this kind of genetically based creature God has actually created as a human being through the evolutionary process," declares Arthur Peacocke.[21] Wolfhart Pannenberg almost celebrates evolution: "the stages of the evolution of life may be seen as the stages of its increasing complexity and intensity and therefore of a growing participation of the creatures in God."[22]

The term *theistic evolution* does not refer to a tightly organized school of thought parallel to either scientific creationism or Intelligent Design.[23] Rather, it refers to a loose federation of theological thinkers who take as their task searching for ways to treat both the science of evolution and the commitments of the Christian faith with integrity. The label, 'theistic evolution', is a tad misleading; because it makes 'evolution' the substantive and 'theistic' the adjective. Yet, the focus here is on divine action in the natural world, not the construction of an alternative to the Darwinian model of evolution. Howard Van Till wants us to see that the God of grace has provided a gifted quality to evolution. "I shall call it *the fully gifted creation perspective*—a vision that recognizes the entire universe as a creation that has, by God's unbounded generosity and unfathomable creativity, been given all of the capabilities for self-organization and transformation necessary to make possible something as humanly incomprehensible as unbroken evolutionary development."[24]

Within the agglomeration of religious thinkers known as theistic evolutionists, some connect God's grace with the doctrine of progress, while others do not. In the late nineteenth and early twentieth centuries, a version of theistic evolution grew up that connected biological evolution with social progress. Accordingly, human spiritual progress replaced the innocence we allegedly possessed before the fall. Ernest William Barnes exemplified the adoption of common decent of humans and apes into a theology of biological and spiritual progress. "Much that is evil in man's passions and appetites is due to natural instincts inherited from an animal ancestry. In fact, man is not a being who has fallen from an ideal state of innocence; he is an animal slowly gaining spiritual understanding and with the gain rising far above his distant ancestors."[25] Following the arrival of the neo-Darwinian synthesis of genetics and natural selection, the non-progressive view has come to reign among scientists. Genetic variation and natural selection are random or indeterminate events, say our scientists—that is, nature grows by trial-and-error. Nature is not guided by a built-in principle of progress.

Among contemporary theistic evolutionists, modes of integrating evolutionary science with faith vary considerably. Some are more progressive, while others are not. Gordon Kaufman is one theologian who attempts to integrate the science of evolution into a theology of progressive development, but without appeal to a God who directly directs evolution. "I propose what I call a biohistorical understanding of the human, one that takes account of, and holds together both the biological grounding of human existence in the web of life on planet Earth and the many different sorts of historical development of humankind in and through the growth, over thousands of generations, of the varied sociocultural patterns of life around the planet."[26] Progress is incorporated into growth here, serendipitously if not divinely guided.

Among the theistic evolutionists who confront squarely our genetic inheritance of a predisposition toward evil and suffering, we find Robert John Russell, founder and director of the Center for Theology and the

Natural Sciences in Berkeley, California. According to Russell's version of "theistic evolution…God creates the world *ex nihilo* with certain fundamental laws and natural constants, and God acts everywhere in time and space as continuous creator (*creatio continua*) in, with, and through the processes of nature. God's action is trustworthy and we describe the results through these laws of nature. The result is the evolution of life. In essence, evolution is how God is creating life."[27]

One of the unique contributions to discussions within theistic evolution is Russell's suggestion that the roots of evil can be found in the physical processes that underlie our inherited biological processes. Original sin originated in our physical substrate, so to speak. "We evolved out of nature with capacities that are both emergent and genuinely new, and yet in some ways based on and continuous with precursor capacities in the animal world that preceded us—like elementary forms of reason and altruistic-like behavior. Perhaps we can look even farther back in the history of life on earth, and even farther down into the physics underlying that history, to find additional precursors (precursors of precursors) that lay the grounds for the eventual possibility of moral behavior in humankind. I call this approach 'the fall without the fall', for it tries to account for the rise of moral behavior, and its brokenness in sin, as genuinely novel in the human species, and yet as arising without a total break in the evolution of humankind from previous forms of life."[28] Our disposition toward sin is rooted in natural evil; and natural evil is rooted in the biology we have inherited from our evolutionary history; and, in addition, this evolutionary history is rooted in a more fundamental and physical set of processes.

Of these physical processes, Russell singles out one, namely, entropy. In thermodynamic systems, of which evolutionary biology is one, the dissipation of energy is inescapable. Entropy is a property of things as they decay, dissolve, and die. "Perhaps, then, we have indeed found a precursor in physics to natural evil: entropy."[29] What we have inherited in our genes was previously inherited from the long history of evolution; and evolution inherited the thermodynamics of death from its physical predecessor, thermodynamics of which one key feature is entropy. What Russell has done is push back the source of what we might think of evil and suffering to a pre-evolutionary stage in cosmic history, to the physics that constrained while making possible the course of biological development. Whether from evolution or from entropy, our propensity for violence and, hence, for inflicting suffering, is something we have inherited.

Russell goes on to say thermodynamics plays a positive role, too, since it underlies the good things in life. It makes evolution possible. Hence thermodynamics is an ambiguous or ambivalent feature of nature, underlying both good and evil in human behavior. No doubt what we experience as evil and suffering derive from an ambiguity built into the substrate of our physical nature.

Our subject matter here is the place of evil and suffering within nature, not progress. Those theistic evolutionists of a previous generation could minimize the impact of evil by taking it up into a progressive worldview, according to which nature will improve and we will eventually graduate from our evil past. Once the doctrine of progress is denied scientifically and the idea of randomness or indeterminateness in nature replaces it, however, the theologian cannot easily rely upon a built-in principle of future redemption. What Russell has offered is an understanding of the biology of evil and suffering that is rooted in physics. This is combined with an understanding of life as rooted in entropy. God is present to us at the physical level—the indeterminate level of quantum activity—argues Russell, even if not requiring the living world to grow according to our standards of progress.

Alternative Answers to the Question of Evolving Evil

How should we answer the theologian's question: where does a God of grace or love or care fit into an evolutionary world? To this one question I can easily suggest three possible answers: (1) naturalism combined with altruism; (2) divine kenosis combined with positing freedom as a higher value than suffering; (3) the Theology of the Cross combined with the theology of new creation. Let us look at them in turn.

The First Answer: Naturalism and Altruism

As we have seen, Richard Dawkins provides the atheistic answer. Nature is without purpose, without meaning, and without care. It is pitiless. Darwin's theory of natural selection demonstrates this point. No divine designer or director or provider is on the scene to add something nature herself does not provide. All that we have is what nature gives us. To ask for anything more would be unreasonable. We should grow up, become reasonable, and simply accept this fact. This need not be reconciled with a God of grace, because no such God exists.

Now, we might ask: what kind of ethic would be based upon such a godless view of evolution? One would expect an ethic of *laissez faire capitalism*, a social ethic that applauds the fittest who defeat their competitors to survive. We would expect racism and genocide. If no God exists and if nature is our only source for moral guidance, then we should expect a Nietzschean ethic that dispenses with the weak and celebrates the "will to power." Yet, this is not the route Dawkins takes us. Rather, Dawkins embraces all the values of the modern Enlightenment: human equality, the pursuit of justice, and even care for the victims of discrimination. Dawkins says that our evolutionary history programmed us not just for survival but also for "the urge to kindness—to altruism, to generosity, to empathy, to pity."[30] And if that is not enough, Dawkins further says that we can overcome our genetic determinism and achieve an ethical standard that transcends our biological inheritance. Now, we might ask, how did we get to this kind of ethic from this kind of natural inheritance? How will we get the leopard to change his spots?

Dawkins distinguishes between the selfish gene and the less-than-selfish organism. Just because genes are selfish, organisms need not be. Selfishness in the Darwinian and Dawkinsian sense is understood simply as the desire to replicate. "A gene is a replicator with high copying-fidelity."[31] Gene replication is the driving force of natural selection. Those genes which get copied and passed on win in the game of survival-of-the-fittest. The genes that survive are those that get copied and repeated.

Now, the organism which the genes have created to carry them from one generation to another need not be selfish in the same way. "We have the power to defy the selfish genes," says Dawkins. We can behave in altruistic ways. We can deliberately cultivate "pure, disinterested altruism—something that has no place in nature."[32]

Dawkins strains to separate the gene from the organism, so that the selfishness of the gene does not automatically transfer to the selfishness of the individual organism. "The whole idea of the selfish gene…is that the unit of natural selection (i.e., the unit of self-interest) is not the selfish organism, nor the selfish group or selfish species or selfish ecosystem, but the selfish *gene*."[33] Then he proceeds to list four ways in which organisms may function altruistically. Even though driven by selfish genes, the social habits of individuals or groups may not in themselves be selfish: (1) *kin altruism* is a form of self-sacrifice on the part of some individuals for other individuals who carry the same DNA, with the result that the shared DNA sequences get passed on; (2) *reciprocal altruism* applies to one group of organisms that cooperate for the benefit of another group which does not share the same DNA, with the result that both groups survive; (3) enhancing social power through conspicuous generosity, resulting in a reputation for dominance or superiority, thereby attracting mates and passing on genes; and (4) employing this reputation for buying advertising within the group, and increasing the opportunity for mating and gene continuance.[34] These final two look a lot alike; both operate at the level of the organism in its respective society, where the chances of its genes' survival are enhanced through the attractiveness or generosity to potential mates.

What Dawkins has established here, in his own mind, is a list of precedents within nature that could lead to a leap in altruism beyond what nature bequeaths to us. We human beings can get beyond the limitations of simply serving the selfish need of the gene. We can cultivate the "urge to kindness—to altruism, to generosity, to empathy, to pity. In ancestral times, we had the opportunity to be altruistic only towards close kin and potential reciprocators. Nowadays, that restriction is no longer there." From a strict Darwinian point of view, was altruism a necessary step in evolutionary development? No. It was a misfire or a mistake, something like an unnecessary mutation. Yet, we can be thankful for such leaps beyond genetic selfishness. Disinterested care for others belongs in the category of "misfirings, Darwinian mistakes: blessed, precious mistakes."[35]

Jesus and Altruism

Dawkins admits that an ethic of self-sacrificial love is non-Darwinian. Can self-sacrificial altruism be reconciled with survival-of-the-fittest?[36] John Teehan tries. He extends the Dawkins logic by applying it to Jesus' apparent denial of reciprocal altruism in favor of loving the other as other. Teehan strives to lodge all morality and all religion in evolutionary biology. Like Dawkins, he wants to deny any transcendent grounding to either morality of religion. Our biological nature is the sole source of our moral values, and religion functions to provide an unnecessary though handy supernatural reinforcement of moral maxims. These moral values and maxims serve reproductive fitness, indirectly guided by kin selection and reciprocal altruism within a cohesive social group. "Religious ethics are grounded in a moral logic that is itself grounded in nature....From an evolutionary perspective religious morality provides a vehicle for extending the evolutionary mechanisms for morality—kin selection and reciprocal altruism."[37]

How might Jesus fit into a biologically grounded system of religious ethics? Jesus appears to defy our genetically determined preference for our own kin and our own in-group. Jesus enjoins us to love God and love others, even if such love is costly to ourselves. Does Jesus advocate a non-reciprocal altruism that contradicts evolutionary morality? Teehan answers no and yes. First, the no. When it comes to Jesus' Golden Rule—to do unto others as you would have them do unto you—Teehan can easily interpret this as tit-for-tat. It is consistent with reciprocal altruism. It serves reproductive fitness. The Golden Rule seems easy to absorb into evolutionary morality.

What about Jesus' teaching that we should love our enemies (Matthew 5:44)? This is more difficult. To love one's enemy means that one risks sacrificing the reproductive fitness of the in-group. When Jesus says, "if anyone strikes you on the right cheek, turn to him the other also" (Matthew 5:39), Teehan can only conclude that such "advice is certainly at variance with the principles of reciprocal altruism."[38] So, how can Teehan lasso Jesus and bring him into the evolutionary corral? By distinguishing between what Jesus taught, on the one hand, and how his disciples have behaved, on the other. Christians simply do not turn the other cheek. Rather, Christians, just like every other religious in-group, defend themselves at the expense of their enemies. "I would claim that the history of Christianity is filled with examples (such as the crusades, the inquisition, and the persecution of heretics and Jews) that speak to the power of the underlying evolutionary logic to overwhelm attempts to develop moral attitudes contrary to it (for example, 'turn the other cheek'). The response of Christians in history to enemies and to attacks has often been much more in line with the psychology of evolutionary morality than with these particular teachings of Jesus. This is not so much a condemnation of Christianity as it is a lesson on the difficulty of moving beyond these evolutionarily ingrained moral predispositions."[39]

What Teehan is saying, in effect, is that the moral values we would expect to rise up from our evolutionary nature would lead to crusades, inquisitions, and persecutions of heretics and Jews. That Jesus taught us to do otherwise places Jesus outside the pale of evolutionary ethics. A non-transcendent ethic rooted in evolution can only expect to further the interests of one's own reproductive fitness by pitting one's in-group against genetic competitors. Both Dawkins and Teehan are naturalists, yet the latter is more willing to remain within a survival-of-the-fittest ethic than the former.

Naturalist philosopher Holmes Rolston III would agree that the roots of our modern ethics lie in our genetic inheritance; but, more than Dawkins or Teehan, Rolston believes human culture transcends our genetic history. "There are precursor animal roots [to ethics], but few will claim that morality is 'nothing but' genetically determined animal behavior."[40] Cultural epigenesis rides on top of biological genesis.

Rolston cautions us to avoid accepting a second best grade of altruism. If one wants to embrace Christian *agape* love in its fullest sense, then no evolutionary precedent can account for it. "A genuinely altruistic sense…a person acts, on the moral account, intending to benefit others at cost to himself or herself, and on the genetic account, increasing the likelihood of the aided person's having offspring over one's having them."[41] Kin altruism or reciprocal altruism are poor substitutes for genuine altruism—*agape* love—because they are secretly forms of the selfish gene in action. "All that natural selection permits is forms of quasi altruism that are actually self-interest."[42] Sociobiologists such as Dawkins and E.O. Wilson have "the problem of generating generosity. Selfish genes are never generous beyond expedience; that is the core of sociobiological theory."[43]

What Rolston, like Dawkins, wants to do is root or ground our highest ethical aspirations in our evolutionary history. Both are naturalists, although Dawkins is the only atheist. Yet, their positions are similar. For Rolston, to move from the drive to survive to self-sacrificial dimensions of a moral ideal is to move from what "is" to what "ought" to be. More than genesis, we need epigenesis. "We inherit these selfish genes, but from somewhere too we inherit genes that prompt us to sympathy, to mutual care, and to cooperation, and from somewhere we…get enough mental power to reflect over our evolutionary genes and to generate an ethic about what *ought* to be in the light of this *is*."[44]

Even though Rolston along with Dawkins and Teehan are naturalists, Rolston is a committed Christian who emphasizes slightly more the extra-genetic advance into cultural determinants for explaining human behavior. When it comes to our propensity for violence, evil, and suffering, Rolston grants that much of this is genetically inherited. Yet, at the cultural level, we humans have turned ordinary killing into the sin of murder combined with the giant proscription: we "ought" to do otherwise. "Human cultural inheritance requires experiences super-to-the-genetic, super-to-the natural, that is, beyond the previous attainment and power of biology.…Killing is not new in the world; primates have killed each other for millennia in the defense of their genetic lines. But murder is new in the world; the human has risen to an option to do otherwise and therefore ought to do otherwise."[45] Theologian Mark Worthing would agree with Rolston. Altruism along with "the sense of sin and the feeling of guilt serve in the first instance to promote and secure the survival of civilization and only secondarily of the species."[46]

If we would wish to construct a theological anthropology with a corresponding ethic on the foundation laid by evolution as the sociobiologists and evolutionary psychologists see it, what would it look like? Charlene P.E. Burns provides an image of expanding circles of altruistic expression. With each ring in the expansion, we get further away from the hegemony of the selfish gene and closer to serving the other as other. "If we read science through the lens of Christian theology…we see an ever-widening altruistic impulse first expressed genetically in the drive toward optimizing survival. The impulse ripples outward in rudimentary forms to find expression as biological altruism, and then gains momentum as it reaches expression in human experience, where the altruistic impulse is now propelled forward through cultural evolution."[47] Such an incorporation of the sociobiological interpretation of altruism assigns to Jesus an evolutionary role. Jesus marks an advance forward in moral progress. "In Jesus, 'the first fruits' of a possible future humanity are revealed. Only now do we perhaps see hints of the next stage of development. As the altruistic drive slowly breaks down the barriers of in-group selection it also has begun to extend its reach beyond the human, to encompass care for other species and for the earth itself."[48]

In summary, what we find in this first alternative is a two step argument. Step one: we observe that nature does not have any values built in from its point of origin. Nature is amoral. It may appear cruel to us, but that is because we look at nature through moral lenses. Step two: we hypothesize that the history of nature has led to the development of a moral consciousness and conscience. We are it. We are the result of an evolutionary process which brought moral judgment to natural history. Through evolution we have risen above our beginnings. Holmes Rolston says, "Morality is not intrinsic to natural systems. In fact, there are no moral agents in wild nature. Nature is amoral, but that is not to disparage it.…Amoral nature is fundamentally and radically the ground, the root out of which arise all the particular values manifest in organisms. This includes all human values, even though, when they come, human values rise higher than their precedents in spontaneous nature."[49]

When theologians try to integrate New Testament commitments with such examples of evolutionary naturalism, Jesus ends up playing the role of the one who introduces an evolutionary advance in altruism. Jesus' ethic of love for the other without expectation of reciprocity is judged to be an advance, yet still on the single evolutionary path. Eliminated is the promise of eschatological transformation as an act of God. In its place we find a version of the train of progress, with the altruism of Jesus as the locomotive.

The Second Answer: Evil as a Means to a Further Good, or, The Free Will Defense

We turn now to the second in our series of three contemporary answers to the evolutionary theodicy question. We turn to one classroom within the larger school of theistic evolutionists, namely, to the kenotic theologians. I try to sum up this position as an appeal to *divine kenosis combined with valuing freedom higher than suffering*. In contrast to naturalism combined with altruism, this answer is theistic. It affirms God as creator. It affirms that God, not nature, is the source and ground of the good.

In its contemporary form, we know this school of thought as kenotic theology. But, somewhat hidden in its own evolutionary development is its ancient predecessor, namely, the Christian concept of evil as the *privatio boni*—that is, the privation of the good. In this theological tradition, what is good is identified with being. The highest good is the fullest being. Subordinate goods can be pressed into the service of higher goods. Let me explain.

It was Augustine who most fully articulated the principle of evil as the privation of the good, *privatio boni*. "For what is that which we call evil but the absence of the good?"[50] One can have something that is purely good, but never something that is purely evil. Evil is always a parasite off what is good, always a distortion or corruption or even destruction of what is good.

According to this North African bishop, to be is to be good. Being is by definition good. To lose being is to lose goodness. To drop from being into nonbeing is to die, to depart from the realm of the good. What we experience in the struggle for survival on an every day basis is the tension between being and nonbeing, between the good that is and its dissolution or disappearance. "Every being, therefore, is a good; a great good, if it cannot be corrupted; a little good, if it can: but in any case, only the foolish or ignorant will deny that it is a good. And if it be wholly consumed by corruption, then the corruption itself must cease to exist, as there is no being left in which it can dwell."[51] This applies to the relationship between health and disease in the animal world. "In the bodies of animals, disease and wounds mean nothing but the absence of health; for when a cure is effected, that does not mean that the evils which were present—namely, the diseases and wounds—go away from the body and dwell elsewhere; they altogether cease to exist; the wound or disease is not a substance, but a defect in the fleshly substance—the flesh itself being a substance and therefore something good, of which those evils—that is, privations of the good which we call healthy—are accidents."[52]

When we turn to the sufferings of the created world, slung in the metaxic tension between being and nonbeing, Augustine affirms what ought always to be thought of as good. Even if we suffer, we are good by virtue of our existence. This applies to all living things. Even in the face of corruption or suffering or dissolution, what we deem evil is redeemed, so to speak, when taken up into the comprehensive ensemble which constitutes the universe in its entirety. Individual suffering is a part of a much larger whole, which is good. "Taken as a whole, however, they are very good, because their *ensemble* constitutes the universe in all its wonderful order and beauty."[53] The beauty of the whole redeems the corruption of the part. The good of the whole of creation redeems the suffering of its individual constituents.

Thomas Aquinas takes this a step further, arguing that what we experience as evil could positively contribute to a richer and fuller good. Evil is a means to an enhanced good end. "If all evil were prevented much good would be absent from the universe. A lion would cease to live if there were no slaying of animals, and there would be no patience of martyrs if there were no tyrannical persecution."[54]

Augustine and Thomas appear to be somewhat sanguine, almost rejoicing at the dialectic between being and nonbeing, between good and evil. Yet, for those of us in a post-Darwinian era, where we are acutely conscious of the overwhelming role played by suffering, death, and extinction, we wrestle. Theologians wrestle with the difficulty of reconciling death with life, destruction with existence, disappearance with redemption. Langdon Gilkey formulates the difficulty in existential terms. "The most baffling and most pressing problem for reflection is the opposition and yet the unity of life and death, of value and the threats to value, of the positive and its negation, of being and of nonbeing. No one escapes this painful and disturbing problem."[55] Can the *privatio boni* come to the rescue?

The flip side of the *privatio boni* is the affirmation that, if it has being, it's good. To exist and to suffer is better than not existing at all. This is a fundamental premise, obviated only by those whose suffering is so grave that they elect suicide to escape it. Might we say that to live even for a short while and suffer is better than to have never lived at all? Will that take care of the theodicy problem?

Kenosis and the Free Will Defense

The *privatio boni* is the background. Now, let's move to the foreground. As contemporary theologians wrestle with the theodicy question in light of evolutionary theory, many put forth the kenosis hypothesis. Our word *kenosis* comes from NRS Philippians 2:5 "Let the same mind be in you that was in Christ Jesus, who, though he was in the form of God, did not regard equality with God as something to be exploited, but emptied himself, taking the form of a slave, being born in human likeness. And being found in human form, he humbled himself and became obedient to the point of death—even death on a cross." To empty oneself or to deny to oneself divinity is that to which the word *kenosis* refers.Note that the kenotic figure here is the second person of the Trinity, the Son, who empties himself of the Father's divinity in order to become incarnate, to suffer, and to die. Jesus Christ de-divinizes himself, so to speak, in order to become Emmanuel, God with us.

Now, does this process of de-divinization apply to the Father? No, not in this text. Might a theologian apply it to the first person of the Trinity? Today's neo-kenotic theologians say, yes. This is the move made by Nancey Murphy and George Ellis. "While the origin of the term was in Christology—it was used to explain how the divine nature could be reconciled with Jesus' humanness—it is now used to refer to God's self-limitation and self-sacrifice and to God's involvement in the suffering of creation."[56] This move leads to two applications of theology to an evolutionary interpretation of creation. By self-limiting, God withdraws both omnipotence and omniscience from the world of creatures, thereby empowering creatures to evolve by natural means. Creatures can create their own world, so to speak; the world engages in self-organization or autopoises. Biological evolution is the form of self-organization this world has taken. Second, as we can see in this quotation, kenosis makes God vulnerable to suffering with the suffering of earth's creatures.

By withdrawing divine power, God opens up space for creatures to exert power. By withdrawing divine power, God opens up space for creaturely freedom. The absence of God is what makes our free activities possible. Jürgen Moltmann puts it this way: "In order to create a world 'outside' himself, the infinite God must have made room beforehand for a finitude in himself. It is only a withdrawal by God into himself that can free the space into which God can act creatively."[57] This creative self-restriction by God makes our contribution to continuing creation possible.

God has created the world with a dynamic interchange of law with chance; and this means God has not pre-programmed every event. Contingency is built right into the dynamics of our world; and contingency is the prerequisite for freedom. What accounts for the specific path that evolution has taken is the contingency and freedom God has provided to the created order. Suffering along the way is a means to a higher good, namely, a community of free individuals. "God purposes to bring about a greater good thereby namely, the kingdom of free-willing, loving persons in communion with God and with each other," is the way Arthur Peacocke puts it.[58] He adds, "This self-limitation is the precondition for the coming into existence of free self-conscious human beings....The cost to God, if we may dare so to speak, was in that act of self-limitation, of *kenosis*, which constitutes God's creative action—a self-inflicted vulnerability to the very processes God had himself created in order to achieve an overriding purpose, the emergence of free persons."[59]

The kenotic God is noncoercive. God allows for the world to exist with freedom. "God's nature is essentially kenotic, as is demonstrated in the life and teaching of Jesus and in particular by his death on the cross,"[60] contend Murphy and Ellis. They go on. "Just as sin is a necessary byproduct of the creation of free and intelligent beings, suffering and disorder are necessary byproducts of a noncoercive creative process that aims at the development of free and intelligent beings."[61] Murphy provides us with the "gist" of this position: "if God is to have living, intelligent, free, loving partners for relationship, then the universe God created had to be almost exactly as it is with respect to the ways in which nature produces human and animal suffering, and in which creatures are limited and subject to imperfections.

Natural and metaphysical evil are unavoidable by-products of choices God had to make in order to achieve his purposes in having creatures who could know, love, and serve him."[62]

This brand of kenotic theology thus handles the theodicy problem by placing suffering and evil on the list of byproducts brought about by the world's own evolutionary self-organization. God did not create suffering and evil. God could not create suffering and evil, because these are the forces of nonbeing. God is responsible for what is, not what is not. With one exception. God's self-withdrawal opens up a cavity of nonbeing into which creaturely contingency and freedom can enter. God made suffering and evil possible, but God did not directly will them as such.

The good toward which all things strive is the creation of intelligent and free human beings. Suffering and evil are the price God was willing to pay for us to evolve, for us to arrive at the point in biohistory where we could respond freely to God in love. God could not program free creatures; because to do so would eliminate the very freedom he desired. All God could do was make freedom possible. We had to do the rest.

Well, not quite. God remains a partner in continuing creation, *creatio continua*. S. Mark Heim lifts our sights to a destiny yet to come. "God determines the world to be undetermined. It is out of God's hands, in the sense that God has freely forsaken the role of being the only decider. But the destiny of creation as a whole is not out of God's hands, for the universal salvific will remains a co-determiner of the ends of *all* creatures."[63] It is not clear here whether God's self-abandonment will continue to enhance our freedom, or whether God will curtail our freedom just to insure that this destiny is attained.

The Kenotic Ethics of the Free Will Defense

Before moving on to a critique of the neo-kenotic position, let us ask: what kind of ethic correlates with a theological anthropology grounded in freedom as the product of evolution? An ethic of genuine altruism or, better, *agape* love? Could it lead to an ethic that takes as its orientation love toward the other for the sake of the other, not expecting any reciprocity?

At Columbia University's Center for the Study of Science and Religion, molecular biologist Robert Pollack provides a minimalist ethic derived from the observation that evolution has led to freedom and that all life forms are interdependent. Our freedom is a gift of biological evolution; and an ethic that extends "the minimum amount of respect and love that is the only fully human relationship" would carry us beyond the "meaninglessness" of evolution's "mechanisms."[64]

Now, can we go further? For a maximalist ethic, Murphy and Ellis add divine kenosis to the explanation for this rise of freedom. Kenosis carries us dramatically further. The kenotic understanding of God's relation to the natural world leads to a human commitment to pacifism. Freely chosen kenotic love entails self-giving; and self-giving entails the refusal to engage in violent behavior. We may even refuse self-defense.

Now, we might ask: would an ethic of self-giving love or even pacifism cohere at all with our inherited propensity for violence? "Given our close connections to animal kin, I do not believe that we could explain how morality ever got off the ground in humans without any precursors in animals," writes Nancey Murphy. However, Murphy does not draw a straight line from our natural precursors to our modern ideal of disinterested love toward our neighbor. A "moral ambiguity of biology" remains inescapable.[65] If we are to know that altruism is actually a good—a good worth sacrificing for—it must be grounded in something more than merely a misfire of Darwinian evolution. It must be grounded in the God who transcends nature. The God Murphy knows is loving in character. She even goes so far as to describe God as kenotically loving, i.e., as self-emptying. "God's nature is essentially kenotic, as is demonstrated in the life and teaching of Jesus and in particular by his death on the cross. The implication is that there should be a kenotic response by men and women who are made in the image of God, mirroring this kenotic nature and reflecting it in their relations to each other and to God."[66]

A Critique of Neo-Kenotic Theology

I would like to mention three criticisms I have of the neo-kenotic approach.[67] First, the new kenotic theologians have yet to articulate a way to make their emphasis on freedom compatible with the idea that we have inherited in our genes the propensity for violence, evil, and suffering. This evolutionary inheritance appears to be a form of genetic determinism, not freedom. If freedom is the alleged divine goal of God's kenotic activity and of nature's self-organizing capacity, then why are we in moral bondage to our genetic past?

Second, I believe the scriptural basis for applying kenosis to the first person of the Trinity and to the doctrine of creation is insufficient. The very passage on which the concept is derived, Philippians 2:5-8, describes the second person divesting himself of the divinity belonging to the first person. No mention of the first person engaging in self-limitation or de-divinizing appears. So, no scriptural warrant exists to apply kenosis to God the Father.

Might one apply kenosis to "God," if by "God" we meant the Godhead, or the Trinity? Well, yes, to be sure. The actions of the Son apply to the actions of God in Godself. If this is what is being said by the kenotic theologians, then they might get by with it.

Even so, we confront a third problem, this time a problem with systematic theology. It has to do with power. It appears that the kenotic theologians make a false assumption about the nature of God's power. They assume that for creatures to have power and hence freedom that God needs to withdraw. If God is omnipotent and possessing all power, then, they assume, we creatures have none. God's omnipotence is a form of tyranny. So, if God withdraws through self-limitation, then we can take advantage of the power vacuum. Only if God lacks power in the world can we have the power to exercise our freedom. For us to be free, God must be absent.

This logic is based upon a false assumption. The neo-kenotic theologians seem to assume that there exists a fixed amount of power in the universe, like there is a fixed number of gallons of gasoline. If God gets more, we get less. If we get more, God gets less. Only if we have enough of what God does not have can we drive our Toyota wherever we choose to go. Perhaps this applies to human drivers, where one person has the power to go further than another. But, I do not believe it applies to God.[68]

When I read scripture, it appears to me that it is the very exertion of God's power that leads to human freedom. God's power empowers us. In the case of the Exodus, for example, God heard the cries of the oppressed slaves in Egypt. God then exerted divine power in order to liberate them from the chains of their taskmasters. NRS Deuteronomy 5:15 "Remember that you were a slave in the land of Egypt, and the LORD your God brought you out from there with a mighty hand and an outstretched arm." Had God decided to be kenotic and withdraw, the Hebrews would have remained helpless in their slavery. Only by exerting power with "a mighty hand and an outstretched arm" could liberation be achieved.

To cite a second example, the Pentecostal experience for Christians today is one of divine empowerment. NRS Acts 1:8 "But you will receive power when the Holy Spirit has come upon you." It appears to me that a Christian theologian should perceive the difference between God's empowerment of us and other more human forms of competitive power. Therefore, it is a mistake, in my judgment, to rewrite the doctrine of creation in such a way that God's absence replaces God's presence in the creative process.

Christopher Southgate offers a criticism similar to mine. If the neo-kenotic theologians presume all power is of a single type and that God and creatures compete for it, then this makes them incompatibilists—that is, they cannot accept the idea that God's actions could be co-present to our creaturely free actions. "It is now my contention that the language of kenosis in creation tends to arise out of commitment to a questionable spatial metaphor for the God-world relation—the alleged need for God to 'make space' within Godself for the created world and/or an also questionable commitment to incompatibilism—the notion that the free actions of creatures are incompatible with the involvement of God in every event."[69]

As Southgate develops his own position within theistic evolution, he applies kenosis within the Trinity to the self-opening of the Father to permit the dynamics of the Son and the creation through the Logos. The intra-trinitarian perichoresis is the foundation for treasuring the particularity of each biological organism, each biological self within creation. He coins the term "selving" to describe this divinely encouraged process. "Selving, then, takes place within what I have called 'deep intratrinitarian kenosis'. It is from the love of the Father for the world, and for the glory of the Son, that other selves gain their existence, beauty and meaning, that which prevents them from collapsing into nothingness. It is from the self-sacrificial love of the Son for the Father and all his works that each created entity gains the distinctive pattern of its existence, that which prevents the creation from collapsing back into an undifferentiated unity. It is from the power of the Spirit, predictable only in its continual creativity and love, which is the same self-transcending and self-renewing love as is between the Father and the Son, that each creature receives its particularity."[70] That which puts the tragedy into an evolutionary theodicy is the observation that many individual creatures never fully selve.

What Southgate has done is pinpoint where he believes evil lodges in the evolutionary process, namely, in the cutting down of individual sentient creatures before they can actualize their potential as selves. That's the evil, the nonbeing. What God does by exerting power in creation, is seek to enhance self-fulfillment. Southgate describes it in Trinitarian terms. "Theologically, we might say that this fulfillment in the creature is the gift of existence from the Father, form and pattern from the Son, particularity from the Holy spirit, and that the creature's praise, in being itself, is offered by the Son to the Father, in the delight of the Spirit."[71]

Is Nature Friend or Foe?

Before proceeding to the third in our list of answers to the evolutionary theodicy question, I would like to pause and ask a different question: how should we understand God as creator and redeemer in light of the nihilism and unfeeling brutality of evolutionary history? On the basis of our observations, does this look like God's world? I ask this because we have inserted into our inquiry the observation that the genes we have inherited from the long history of natural selection dispose us at minimum to competition if not violence, evil, and suffering. Is this the best we can say? On balance, is this a world unrecognizable from a theological point of view?

Let us ask the question this way: is the natural world our friend or foe? Friend, is the answer given by both an atheist and a theologian. Atheist Richard Dawkins answers: "We live not only on a friendly planet but also in a friendly universe."[72] Theologian Philip Hefner gives us the same answer, even if he adds a bit of drama: "The creation-doctrine is an item of faith, because in the absence of any final demonstration or disproof, faith affirms that the created world, including ourselves, *is* God's creation—that it is finally friend, not foe; cosmos, not chaos; consummation, not dissolution."[73] Curiously, Dawkins bases his conclusion on scientific evidence gathered into the Anthropic Principle. Hefner bases his judgment on faith, even if on occasion the evidence might appear to be contrary. Different methods. Same conclusion.

William Stoeger belongs in the nature-as-friend camp. What we experience as evil finds its place in a larger scheme that works for the good. "In a dynamic evolving universe, which is also limited in resources, relatively integral and autonomous in its functioning, relational and interconnected, and open at every stage to further higher-level organization, the fragility, transience and dissolution of individual objects and systems are essential.... Thus, transience, fragility, dissolution and death, while certainly 'natural evils' form the limited point of view of those organisms and objects which vanish, are obvious 'goods' in the long term for nature itself."[74] And, yes, our evolutionary heritage orients human beings toward "selfishness," toward sin.[75] Still, Stoeger places evolution within the framework of "God's universal creative action in nature, and God's special action in history."[76] What we experience as natural evil is taken up into God's more comprehensive and gracious action in the created world.

This would seem to be God's message to Job, spoken from the whirlwind. Immanuel Kant interprets Job this way: "These things by themselves can serve some purpose but in relationship to other beings and especially to man, they are destructive, run against all purposes, and do not seem to agree with the idea of a plan established with wisdom and goodness. Even through these things, God showed to Job an ordering of the whole which manifests a wise Creator, although his ways remain inscrutable for us."[77] It is the inscrutability that makes reconciling the brutality of nature "red in tooth and claw" with a wise divine mind and a loving divine heart. The reconciliation of the brutal part with the healing whole lies beyond our ability to discern; yet faith beyond the visible evidence calls us to trust that this is so.

What we have done here in this brief interlude is place victims of suffering and the human propensity for sin within a more inclusive context, namely, the created world of nature as friend, not foe. Creation, after all, is a gift of God's grace.

The Third Answer: A Theology of the Cross and Resurrection

Now, to the third answer to our evolutionary theodicy question: where does a God of grace or love or care fit into an evolutionary world? In this section I would like to nourish a seed that was sown by Arthur Peacocke and Nancey Murphy in the kenotic theology section, namely, that God is vulnerable to suffering with the creation. To this I would like to add the New Testament emphasis on promise. What is promised is a new creation. How, I ask, might the promise of a new creation affect our image of the present one?[78]

First, the matter of divine suffering. Does it make sense, as Whitehead once said, to think: "God is the great companion, the fellow sufferer who understands"?[79] Yes, it does. It certainly makes sense when we turn to the *Theology of the Cross.* In what follows, I will attempt to interpret the natural world in light of the Theology of the Cross.

In the Reformation theology of Martin Luther and its subsequent development in Jürgen Moltmann, the theology of the cross stresses two messages. First, it is a theory of revelation, revelation hidden behind masks. It insists that God's presence and action in the world are not immediately visible. To the contrary, what God actually does might differ from what we expect. God is hidden. God's majesty and power are hidden behind the masks of humility and weakness. God's eternal life is hidden behind the mask of death, healing behind a mask of suffering. "The manifest and visible things of God are placed in opposition to the invisible, namely, his human nature, weakness, foolishness…in the humility and shame of the cross."[80] To understand God, says Luther, we must look at the cross and recognize that we do not understand God.

The message coming through the cross is the one relevant to our discussion here, namely, God's life shares in the suffering of the world. In the person of Jesus, the triune God suffers. "When the crucified Jesus is called the 'image of the invisible God'," writes Jürgen Moltmann, "the meaning is that *this* is God, and God is like *this*.…The Christ event on the cross is a God event."[81] Can we say that all the suffering of this world is taken up in this representative person, Jesus Christ? Yes. As the universal logos, the principle by which all things hold together, the actual history of the creation complete with all of its suffering is taken up into the life of the second person of the Trinity, the Son. Jesus Christ is both the embodiment of the physical world and the image of God. God experiences what we experience, both suffering and estrangement.

What the theologian needs to do here is make a move from history to nature, actually to the history of nature. When we speak of the crucifixion of Jesus, we ordinarily think of it as a historical event. It is a human event, a political event. But, in dealing with evolutionary theodicy, we might ask, could the cross be a natural event as well? Could we apply what we learn about God from the cross to how we understand the natural world, and even how we understand human nature?

Jürgen Moltmann would provide a "yes" answer. "If Christ is the first-born of the dead, then he cannot be merely 'the new Adam' of a new humanity. He must also be understood as the firstborn of the whole creation. He is present not only in the human victims of world history, but in victimized nature too."[82] The cross applies to the natural domain just as it does to the human or historical domain.

Another kindred theologian, George L. Murphy, also answers "yes." Murphy sees the cross as a pattern with which to interpret creation. "The crosslike pattern of creation means that Christ crucified has cosmic significance."[83] Murphy goes on: "God suffers *with* the world from whatever evil takes place....We begin with the fact that God suffered on the cross, but we do not have to stop with that. God's voluntary self-limitation that enables the world to have its own existence and integrity keeps God from simply preventing all evil in miraculous ways. Evil is then the 'dark side' of an aspect of the goodness of creation, its functional integrity."[84]

Now, as you can see, George Murphy like Nancey Murphy [there is no family connection] falls into the kenotic trap. What I would like to borrow from both Murphys is the cosmic application of the Theology of the Cross, minus the "self-limitation" on God's part. As I see it, the entering of God into the world to share in its suffering is an expression of God's power as well as God's love; it is not the result of a divine self-withdrawal.

I believe we can benefit from the realism that results from the Theology of the Cross. It helps us to face our own human nature without recourse to denial or moral self-justification. What we learn about God from the cross teaches us about facing the truth about ourselves. God does not require triumph and victory along with the genocide of enemies to accomplish the divine will. The cross does not bless survival-of-the-fittest as a moral category. Yet, we live in part with the gifts bequeathed to us by those who survived and made our life possible. We are the fruit growing in the garden of natural selection. This theological realism permits us to face the reality about ourselves as human beings. We must face the fact that, as the German text of the Augsburg Confession says, "all human beings who are born in the natural way are conceived and born in sin. This means that from birth they are full of evil lust and inclination and cannot by nature possess true fear of God and true faith in God."[85]

Invoking the Theology of the Cross only gets us half way home. What it does is make clear that if we begin with what we know about God based upon revelation in the cross of Jesus Christ, God is likely to identify as much with the victims of predation and natural selection as with the victors. If this provides a clue to the meaning of creation, we cannot allow inclusive fitness or triumphal progress to define in any exclusive fashion God's providence in the evolution of life. Yet, there must be more. There must be a vision of what the "good" in creation is (Genesis 1:1-2:4a), which we may apply. This vision is found in the symbol of the new creation.

Resurrection and New Creation

The *new creation* is a natural symbol, because we associate creation with nature. More frequently the Bible uses historical or political symbols such as the "kingdom of God" or "the new Jerusalem" when identifying God's redemptive plan. Yet, the natural symbols and political symbols are interchangeable. Both point to God's eschatological promise of a new order, a renewed creation which will also be salvation.[86]

Isaiah's prophecy of what we have nicknamed the "Peaceable Kingdom" stands right up and demands notice. [NRS] Isaiah 11:6 "The wolf shall live with the lamb, the leopard shall lie down with the kid, the calf and the lion and the fatling together, and a little child shall lead them. The cow and the bear shall graze, their young shall lie down together; and the lion shall eat straw like the ox. The nursing child shall play over the hole of the asp, and the weaned child shall put its hand on the adder's den." When the Messiah comes to establish God's kingdom, all of nature will participate in a cosmic healing. There will be peace among the animals. No longer will they devour one another to assuage their hunger. No longer will their species compete with one another for survival. No longer will we in the human race find ourselves at enmity with the nature that surrounds us. Might the theologian say: this is the creation God intended to call "good" back in Genesis 1:1-2:4a?[87]

This eschatological image of peace in the animal kingdom raises the question of the scope of new creation. Is it distinctively human? Or, does it encompass all of creation? Redemption in Christian theology does not target *homo sapiens* alone. It targets all of creation, including the animals whom we eat and cuddle in our homes. Russian Orthodox theologian, Vladimir Lossky, places us within the full context. "On his way to union with God, man in no way leaves creatures aside, but gathers together in his love the whole cosmos disordered by sin, that it may at last be transfigured by grace."[88]

Like Lossky, John Polkinghorne welcomes animals into the new creation. "On the one hand, I cannot imagine that there will be no animals in the new creation. That would be an impoverished world. On the other hand, I think it highly unlikely that they will all be there. There is a human intuition, shared by many but not by all, that animals are indeed to be valued, but more in the type than in the token....An intriguing special case is presented by animals who are greatly loved pets. Have they acquired sufficient idiosyncratic significance to require this to be continued beyond death? I do not know. There comes a time when it is best to call a halt to eschatological speculation and to heed the advice, 'wait and see'."[89] Southgate is unhappy with Polkinghorne's substitution of the "type" for the individual animal. He "rejects Polkinghorne's conclusion that animals are only representatives of their types, and considers instead their individual suffering."[90] Redemption, for Southgate, involves the subjectivity and fulfillment of the animal self, as an individual.

Isaiah's vision of the Peaceable Kingdom is complemented by New Testament prophecy. The final book in the Christian Bible, the Apocalypse, provides a parallel prophecy in the form of a vision of the New Jerusalem. Although the *polis* of God is drawn from a pool of political metaphors, it includes the natural order. Healing takes place. Disease will disappear. So will other forms of suffering. NRS Revelation 21:1 "Then I saw a new heaven and a new earth; for the first heaven and the first earth had passed away, and the sea was no more. And I saw the holy city, the new Jerusalem, coming down out of heaven from God, prepared as a bride adorned for her husband. And I heard a loud voice from the throne saying, "See, the home of God is among mortals. He will dwell with them; they will be his peoples, and God himself will be with them; he will wipe every tear from their eyes. Death will be no more; mourning and crying and pain will be no more, for the first things have passed away." When confronting the theodicy question, I find these two prophetic passages to provide the key to the answer, because they indicate how wholeness and healing belong to the heart of the divine plan.

May we apply these eschatological symbols to the doctrine of creation? May we think of the present creation as on the way, so to speak, to a new creation that will deserve the unambiguous title, "very good"?

As important as the Theology of the Cross is here, it would dissolve into pathos without being coupled to new creation. With some force, Jürgen Moltmann says that evolution needs redemption. "A *Christus volutor* without *Christus redemptor* is nothing other than a cruel, unfeeling *Christus selector*, a historical world-judge without compassion for the weak…There is therefore no meaningful hope for the future of creation unless 'the tears are wiped from every eye'. But they can only be wiped out when the dead are raised, and when the victims of evolution experience justice through the resurrections of nature. Evolution in its ambiguity has no such redemptive efficacy and therefore no salvific significance either. If Christ is to be thought of in conjunction with evolution, he must become evolution's redeemer."[91]

For a theologian to deal adequately with the Darwinian model of evolution complete with predator-prey violence and the massive history of extinction, the doctrine of redemption must be brought to bear on the doctrine of creation. Robert John Russell recommends this with considerable force. "We need to relocate the problem of natural evil from the doctrine of creation to the doctrine of redemption, where we can find appropriate forms of response shaped by the millennia of theology's grappling with the problem of moral evil. In short, we need to extend the Theology of the Cross and the Resurrection of Jesus to embrace all of life on earth—and in the universe."[92] William Stoeger would concur. "The resolution of the problem of evil demands the perspective of the eschatological completion of creation in the ultimate domination of good over evil and life over death and diminishment."[93]

Where in the World is God?

When we are confronted by a difficult problem that resists a satisfying solution, we might ask ourselves: are we formulating the question appropriately? Is it appropriate to ask: can we reconcile the dynamics of the long history of the evolutionary process with a theology based upon the cross and resurrection of Jesus Christ? The answer to this inquiry has not come easily. Yet, I am not confident there is a way to alter the question to insure a more simple answer. So, I have pressed forward with this form of the question.

By relying on the third of the three alternative answers to the theodicy question raised by evolutionary theory, my suggested logic has been this: when a disciple with faith looks upon the cross of Jesus Christ, something about God is revealed. One quality revealed is that God in Godself is present to us under the conditions of rejection, suffering, and death. If we insist on believing that a God of power sides only with victory, then God's presence under the conditions of the cross will elude us. Yet, if we can confess that in the man from Nazareth we perceive the universal *logos* incarnate, and if we perceive that he sums up in himself all the sufferings of the created order, then the sufferings of this world become internal to the divine life.

By joining with others willing to admit they adhere to *theistic evolution*, I have turned to the cross and resurrection of Jesus Christ. Rather than keep all speculative theology within the doctrine of creation, I have asked whether the doctrine of redemption could be equally illuminating on the difficult question of evil and suffering. I have answered in the affirmative.

It was Alfred Tennyson (1809-1892) who penned the line that gives rise to the theodicy problem in evolution; he wrote that nature is blood "red in tooth and claw." In the very same poem, *In Memoriam*, Tennyson could also lift up an eschatological vision.

> That God, which ever lives, and loves,
> One God, one law, one element,
> And one far-off divine event,
> To which the whole creation moves.

Beginning with the cross one might ask: can what we have learned about God's love and grace through divine revelation in the cross apply to our expanding knowledge of nature's evolutionary history? Because the story of Jesus is the story of God's incarnation entailing the taking up of the human experience of injustice and suffering into the divine life, would it follow that in nature God identifies with the victims of unfitness? Would it follow from Jesus' Easter resurrection that we have reason to believe the future will be different from the past, that eschatologically the lion will lie down with the lamb? Yes.

Notes

1. Theodosius Dobzhansky, *Genetics of the Evolutionary Process* (New York: Columbia University Press, 1970) 5-6.
2. Ann Milliken Pederson and Phillip Hefner, "Reforming Theology, Reframing Science," *Dialog,* 46:3 (Fall 2007) 216.
3. Charles Darwin, *The Origin of Species by Means of Natural Selection* (London, John Murray, 6th ed., 1872) IV.
4. Ibid., XV.
5. "Modern biology described suffering as a necessary tool for living creatures to orient themselves in realty, or as by-products of this capacity," writes Ulf Görman; "and death is necessary for evolution through variation and selective retention." "Introduction" to *Design and Disorder: Perspectives from Science and Theology*, edited by Niels Henrik Gregersen and Ulf Görman (London and New York: T. & T. Clark, 2002) 5.
6. Stephen Jay Gould, "Darwin and Paley Meet the Invisible Hand," *Natural History* (November 1980) 8.
7. Michael Ruse, "Darwinism: Foe or Friend?" in *The Evolution of Rationality:*

Interdisciplinary Essays in Honor of J. Wentzel van Huyssteen, edited by F. LeFron Shults (Grand Rapids: William B. Eerdmans, 2006) 231.

8. Francisco J. Ayala, *Darwin's Gift to Science and Religion* (Washington DC: Joseph Henry Press, 2007) xi.

9. Charles Darwin, *The Life and Letters of Charles Darwin, Including an Autobiographical Chapter,* edited by his son, Francis Darwin, 3 Volumes (London: John Murray, 1888) 2:311. Darwin's disciple, Thomas Huxley, also wrestled with the theodicy problem, solving it by eliminating God while decrying evil and suffering in nature. "Evil stares us in the face on all sides; that if anything is real, pain and sorrow and wrong are realities." *Evolution and Ethics* (Amherst NY: Prometheus, 1896, 2004) 71. Neither Darwin nor Huxley sought to solve the theodicy problem by dubbing nature morally neutral.

10. Richard Dawkins, *River Out of Eden: A Darwinian View of Life* (New York: Harper, Basic, 1995) 95-96. The absence of purpose or meaning is the most significant challenge evolutionary theory poses to religious sensibilities. In the words of Terry D. Cooper, "*all* religious traditions are in trouble if the universe is pointless and without any overarching meaning. A purposeless universe is certainly a Godless universe." *Dimensions of Evil* (Minneapolis: Fortress Press, 2007) 45.

11. Christopher Southgate, "Creation as *Very Good* and *Groaning in Travail*: An Exploration in Evolutionary Theodicy," *The Evolution of Evil*, edited by Gaymon Bennett, Martinez Hewlett, Ted Peters, and Robert John Russell (Göttingen: Vandenhoeck & Ruprecht, 2008) 53-85. A related problem to the one I am addressing here is whether pre-human evolutionary history provides precursors to human sinning. If this is the case, then animal behavior we witness today should demonstrate at least proto-sin. Denis Edwards is a theologian who would deny that such phenomena as animal territorialism or aggression (disordered behavior) is sin. *The God of Evolution: A Trinitarian Theology* (New York: Paulist Press, 1999) 65. Mark Worthing replies rhetorically, "But if this is not sin, then what, according to the theological tradition is sin?" "The Emergence of Guilt and 'Sin' in Human Evolution: A Theological Reflection," in *Sin and Salvation: Task of Theology Today III*, ed. by Duncan Reid and Mark Worthing (Adelaide: ATF Press, 2003) 116.

12. Henry M. Morris, *The Genesis Record: A Scientific and Devotional Commentary on the Book of Beginnings* (Grand Rapids: Baker, 1976) 79.

13. This variant of theistic evolution is spelled out in Ted Peters and Martinez Hewlett, *Evolution from Creation to New Creation* (Nashville: Abingdon Press, 2003).

14. Richard Wrangham and Dale Peterson: *Demonic Males: Apes and the Origins of Human Violence* (Boston and New York: Houghton Mifflin, Mariner Books, 1996) 198. The difference between human DNA and Chimp DNA is only 1.23%. See: Michael D. Lemonick and Andrea Dorfman, "What Makes Us Different? *Time* 168:15 (9 October, 2006) 44-53.

15. Jonathan Marks, *What it Means to be 98% Chimpanzee* (Berkeley: University of California Press, 2002) 160.

16. Robert Wright, *The Moral Animal* (New York: Pantheon Books, 1994) 151. Paleontologist Daryl P. Domning and Monika K. Hellwig find they can thank evolutionary theory for enhancing the concept of original sin. "Far from

undermining the concept of original sin…the evolutionary perspective underlies both its truth value and its practical relevance as never before." *Original Selfishness: Original Sin and Evil in Light of Evolution* (Aldershot, UK: Ashgate, 2006) 5.

17. Patricia A. Williams, *Doing without Adam and Eve: Sociobiology and Original Sin* (Minneapolis: Fortress Press, 2001) 134.

18. Ibid., xv. Williams does away with the historical Adam and Eve when incorporating evolutionary genetics into her concept of original sin. Can one keep both while denying evolution? Theologian Charles E. Warren, repudiates evolutionary theory while still affirming a genetic influence (not genetic determinism) on human sin. Affirming a historical Adam and Eve, he holds that in our fallen state our genes have been altered by God so as to lead us toward death. This is consistent with St. Augustine's doctrine of original sin, says Warren. "Augustine clearly asserts that the biological impulses or desires of the body are at times vicious, inciting one to vice, and are but manifestations of the corruption of the flesh resulting from Adam's first sin.…Genetic science clearly serves as the handmaiden of theology and not as its adversary." *Original Sin Explained? Revelations from Human Genetic Science* (Lanham: University Press of America, 2002) 132-133.

19. James E. Waller, "The Ghost in the Machine," *Science and Theology News,* (July/August 2006) 28.

20. Ibid.

21. Arthur Peacocke, "The Challenge and Stimulus of the Epic of Evolution to Theology," in *Many Worlds: The New Universe, Extraterrestrial Life, and the Theological Implications,* edited by Steven Dick (Philadelphia and London: Templeton Foundation Press, 2000) 99.

22. Pannenberg, *Systematic Theology,* 2:133.

23. For a comprehensive survey of the various religious interpretations of evolution including theistic evolution, see Peters and Hewlett, *Evolution from Creation to New Creation.*

24. Howard J. Van Till, "The Fully Gifted Creation," in *Three Views on Creation and Evolution,* edited by J. P. Moreland and John Mark Reynolds (Grand Rapids MI: Zondervan Publishing House, 1999) 173.

25. Ernest William Barnes, *Should Such a Faith Offend? Sermons and Addresses* (London: Hodder and Stoughton, 1927) 312-313, cited in Peter J. Bowler, *Monkey Trials and Gorilla Sermons: Evolution and Christianity from Darwin to Intelligent Design* (Cambridge MA and Lonon UK: Harvard University Press, 2007) 170.

26. Gordon D. Kaufman, *God, Mystery, Diversity* (Minneapolis: Fortress Press, 1996) 74.

27. Russell, *Cosmology, Evolution, and Resurrection Hope*, 28.

28. Ibid., , 30-31.

29. Ibid., 33. See: Robert John Russell, *Cosmology from Alpha to Omega* (Minneapolis: Fortress Press, 2008).

30. Dawkins, *God Delusion*, 221.

31. Dawkins, *Selfish Gene*, 30.

32. Ibid., 215.

33. Dawkins, *God Delusion*, 215.

34. Ibid., 219-220. For more on the relation of kin altruism to reciprocal altruism,

see: Robin Dunbar, "Social Behaviour and Evolutionary Theory," *The Cambridge Encyclopedia of Human Evolution*, edited by Steve Jones, Robert Martin, and David Pilbeam (Cambridge: Cambridge University Press, 1992) 145-147.

35. Dawkins, *God Delusion.*, 221.

36. Can psychological altruism, understood as concern for the welfare of others regardless of its role in one's own reproductive fitness, be seen as an outgrowth of evolutionary mechanisms? Yes, say Elliott Sober and David Sloan Wilson. "An ultimate concern for the welfare of others is among the psychological mechanisms that evolved to motivate adaptive behavior." *Unto Others: The Evolution and Psychology of Unselfish Behavior* (Cambridge and London: Harvard University Press, 1998) 7. Wilson's criticism of Dawkins is that group selection needs to supplement gene (individual) selection if evolutionary theory is to account for culture, especially religion. "Beyond Demonic Memes: Why Richard Dawkins is Wrong About Religion," *The Skeptic* (July 4, 2007) http://www.skeptic.com/eskeptic/07-07-04.html

37. John Teehan, "The Evolutionary Basis of Religious Morality," *Zygon* 41:3 (September 2006) 748, 758.

38. Ibid., 763.

39. Ibid., 763.

40. Holmes Rolston, III, *Genes, Genesis, and God: Values and their Origins in Natural and Human History* (Cambridge: Cambridge University Press, 1999) 228.

41. Ibid., 248.

42. Ibid., 251.

43. Ibid., 267.

44. Ibid., 269.

45. Ibid., 301.

46. Worthing, "The Emergence of Guilt and Sin in Human Evolution, 122.

47. Charlene P.E. Burns, "Self-Sacrificial Love: Evolutionary Deception of Theological Reality?" *Cross Currents,* 57:1 (Spring 2007) 112.

48. Ibid., 114.

49. Rolston, *Genes, Genesis, and God,* 286-287.

50. Augustine, *The Enchiridion on Faith, Hope, and Love* (Washington DC: Regnery Gateway, 1961) XI, p. 11.

51. Ibid., XII, p.13.

52. Ibid., XI, p.11.

53. Ibid., X, p.11.

54. Thomas Aquinas, *Summa Theologica,* First Part, Q.22: A.2.

55. Langdon Gilkey, *Nature, Reality, and the Sacred: The Nexus of Science and Religion* (Minneapolis: Fortress Press, 1993) 189.

56. Nancey Murphy and George F.R. Ellis, *On the Moral Nature of the Universe* (Minneapolis: Fortress Press, 1996) 175.

57. Jürgen Moltmann, *God in Creation* (San Francisco: Harper, 1985) 86. Pannenberg is critical of Moltmann. "The different interpretation of 'nothing' by J. Moltmann, which rests on Jewish speculation and which identifies it as the space that God gives creatues as he himself withdraws....must also be rejected as a materially unfounded

mystificaiton of the subject." *Systematic Theology,* 2: 14-15.

58. Peacocke, "Challenge," 108.

59. Arthur Peacocke, *Theology for a Scientific Age* (Minneapolis: Fortress Press, 1993) 123-124. At points Pannenberg takes up the free will defense. "The Creator accepts the risk of sin and evil as a condition of realizing the goal of a free fellowship of the creatures with himself. God did not will wickedness and evil as such. He could nto take pleasure in them. They are not an object of his will." *Sytematic Theology*, 2: 167. Yet, we might ask: is freedom worth the cost? Philip Kitcher rhetorically registers doubt. "Darwin's account of the history of life greatly enlarges the scale on which suffering takes place: through millions of years, billions of animals experience vast amounts of pain, supposedly so that, after an enormous number of extinctions of entire species, on the tip of one twig of the evolutionary tree, there may emerge a species with the special properties that make us able to worship the Creator." "Darwin and Democracy," *Cross Currents,* 57:1 (Spring 2007) 22.

60. Murphy and Ellis, 94.

61. Ibid., 247.

62. Nancey Murphy, "Science and the Problem of Evil: Suffering as a By-product of a Finely Tuned Cosmos," in *Physics and Cosmology: Scientific Perspectives on the Problem of Natural Evil,* edited by Nancey Murphy, Robert John Russell, and William R. Stoeger (Vatican City State and Berkeley: Vatican Observatory and the Center for Theology and the Natural Sciences, 2007) 140.

63. S. Mark Heim, *The Depth of the Riches: A Trinitarian Theology of Religious Ends* (Grand Rapids MI: William B. Eerdmans, 2001) 77.

64. Robert Pollack, "Intelligent Design, Natural Design, and the Problem of Meaning in the Natural World," *Cross Currents,* 57:1 (Spring 2007) 134-135.

65. Murphy, "Is Altruism Good?"

66. Murphy and Ellis, 194.

67. I refer to this contemporary school as "neo-kenotic" because in late nineteenth century Germany a school of "kenotic theology" appeared briefly.

68. One might interpret Pannenberg as opposing the assumptions at work in this kenotic interpretation of divine omnipotence. "It is easy…to be misled by the abstract idea of unlimited power into a confusion of God's lordship with the excessive omnipotence of tyranny. This misunderstanding arises when we set God's power as omnipotence in antithesis to others who have power.…But the power of God has no precondition outside itself. One of its features is that it brings forth that over which it has power. Only as the Creator can God be almighty.…as the acts of the Creator they are still oriented beyond destruction to the life of his creatures." *Systematic Theology,* 1:416. Yet, elsewhere, Pannenberg interprets the kenosis of the Son within the Trinitarian life as the initiation of a creation distinct from the Father. "This self-emptying of the Son (Phil. 2:6-7) is also to be understood as the self-actualizing of the deity of the Trinitarian God in its relation to the world that comes into being thereby." Ibid., 421. The Father surrenders his lordship to permit distinction and freedom for the creation.

69. Southgate, "Creation."

70. Ibid.

71. Ibid.
72. Dawkins, *God Delusion*, 141.
73. Philip J. Hefner, "Creation," in *Christian Dogmatics,* edited by Carl E. Braaaten and Robert W. Jenson (2 Volumes: Minneapolis: Fortress Press, 1984) 1:356.
74 William R. Stoeger, S.J., "Evolution, God and Natural Evil," *Can Nature Be Evil or Evil Natural?* edited by Cornel W. Du Toit (Pretoria: University of South Africa, 2006) 25.
75. Ibid., 26.
76. Ibid., 18.
77. Immanuel Kant, "On the Failure of all Attempted Philosophical Theodices," tr. Michel Despland in Michel Despland, ed., *Kant on History and Religion* (Montreal: McGill-Queen's University Press, 1973) 292-293.
78. As we move from creation to new creation, we must ask if within our evolutionary history we can find a precursor or a prolepsis of the transformation yet to come. Christians locate the anticipatory sign of the new creation in Jesus' Easter resurrection, which functions for us as a promise. Can fragmentary but authentic gestures of transformatory love in the animal world and in human caring also provide a precursor for God's future? "Within our natural this-worldly limitations there is possible a foreshadowing of that in which we believe, redemption." Hans Schwarz, "Salvation in the Otherwordly," *Sin and Salvation*, 236.
79. Alfred North Whitehead, *Process and Reality,* Corrected Edition, edited by David Ray Griffin and Donald W. Sherburne (New York: Macmillan, Free Press, 1929, 1978) 351. What Whitehead shares in common with the Theology of the Cross is the acknowledgment that God is capable of suffering with creatures. However, redemption for Whitehead dissolves the subjectivity of the creatures into the objective immortality of God's life. What is implied in the Theology of the Cross when combined with the theology of new creation is that the subjectivity of the creatures, even when suffering, is precious to God; and creaturely subjectivity is not only healed but becomes everlasting in the new creation.
80. *Luther's Works*, 31: 53. Like me, Charlene P. E. Burns appropriates Luther's Theology of the Cross to deal with the theodicy problem in nature; yet, her emphasis is different. Rather than emphasize God's suffering with the victims of survival-of-the-fittest, Burns uses Luther to emphasize that the hidden God is responsible for the suffering and evil in creation. We must accept this, rather than try to wish it away. "The problem for a theologian is how to take up the call for honesty about God and the indifference of the universe to suffering while remaining faithful to Christian claims that God is Creator, Sustainer and Self-Giving Love." "Honesty about God: Theological Reflections on Violence in an Evolutionary Universe," *Theology and Science* 4:3 (November 2006) 280.
81. Jürgen Moltmann, *The Crucified God* (San Francisco: Harper, 1974) 205.
82. ürgen Moltmann, *The Way of Jesus Christ* (San Francisco: Harper, 1990) 278-279. Protestants are not the only ones who appeal to the cross when interpreting divine atonement for the natural domain. So also do Roman Catholic theologians such as Denis Edwards. See his *God of Evolution,* 36-42; and "Every Sparrow that Falls to the Ground: The Cost of Evolution and the Christ Event," *Ecotheology* 111 (March

2006) 103-123.

83. George L. Murphy, *The Cosmos in Light of the Cross* (Harrisburg PA: Trinity Press International, 2003) 33.

84. Ibid., 87. Celia Deane-Drummond cautions against viewing nature with a built in cruciform structure. She fears that if we view the historic cross of Jesus as one instance of a prior natural structure, the result will be a fatalistic acceptance of natural suffering. Deane-Drummond wants the cross to provide a challenge to, not an endorsement of, suffering. "The Evolution of Sin and the Redemption of Nature," an unpublished paper delivered as part of the J. K. Russell Fellowship at the Center for Theology and the Natural Sciences, March 31, 2007.

85. Augsburg Confession, Article II, *The Book of Concord: The Confessions of the Evangelical Lutheran Church,* edited by Robert Kolb and Timothy J. Wengert (Minneapolis: Fortress Press, 2000) 36-38.

86. Note that I am not appealing to emergence to deal with the theodicy problem. In current discussion, we understand 'emergence' to refer to "the theory that cosmic evolution repeatedly includes unpredictable, irreducible, and novel appearances." Philip Clayton, *Mind and Emergence: From Quantum to Consciousness* (Oxford and New York: Oxford University Press, 2004) 39. Emergence may provide a naturalistic explanation for novelty, but not redemption. It could inadvertently justify survival-of-the-emergent-fittest, but not empathize with the Psalmist, "Out of the depths I cry to you…" (Psalm 130:1). At this point, Antje Jackelėn sees a disconnect between emergence and theology. "Emergence Everywhere! Reflections on Philip Clayton's *Mind and Emergence,*" *Zygon* 41:3 (September 2006) 630. In my judgment, eschatology requires more than emergence can deliver. "There cannot be any scientific justification for theological eschatology precisely because it would be a contradiction in itself to treat aspects of eschatology, such as the resurrection of the dead and the New Creation, which by definition are rooted in divine initiative, as if they were a preprogrammed aspect of evolution." Antje Jackelėn, *Time and Eternity* (Philadelphia and London: Templeton Foundation Press, 2005) 208.

87. Nicola Hoggard Creegan argues that the Darwinian reliance upon natural selection makes evolutionary theory too stringently anti-theological. It would be better to open the window of evolutionary science to sense the presence of the creative God. Yet, something short of a full revelation would result. "If we interact with and adopt some aspecs of the new bilogy we find that older teleological aspects of creation are more evident, and we can regain some confidence that the work of God in forming creation is not utterly obscured. This overcomes some of the distance natural selection has placed between us and nature as God's creation… God's work is evident, but God will be seen never directly but always peripherally. God is a revealing and concealing God, although there is perfection hidden in the universe that seems to point to its eschatological resolution." "A Christian Theology of Evolution and Participation," *Zygon* 42:2 (June 2007) 516. She adds: "Taking seriously the partly hidden nature of God, then, would mediate between deism and an intelligent design position. It would affirm more possibility of seeing God in nature than do Haught, Moltmann, and Peters but less than the advocates of intelligent design." 509.

88. Vladimir Lossky, *The Mystical Theology of the Eastern Church* (London: J. Clarke, 1957) 111.
89. John Polkinghorne, *Science and the Trinity* (New Haven: Yale University Press, 2004) 152.
90. Southgate, "Creation."
91. Moltmann, *Way of Jesus Christ*, 296-297. Charlene Burns might be critical of the position I am developing here. Whereas I emphasize the promise of divine transformation in the future, she emphasizes a human commitment to altruism and co-redemption of nature in the present. "A focus on the future…tends to re-inscribe the perennial problem that all faiths that posit reward in the after-life face: how do we avoid discounting the importance of working to alleviate suffering here-and-now if it is not really real? Theologies of evolution must not lose sight of the reality of either past or future." "Honesty about God," 286.
92. Robert John Russell, "Five Key Topics on the Frontier of Theology and Science Today," *Dialog* 46:3 (Fall 2007) 204.
93. Stoeger, "Evolution, God, and Natural Evil," 33. In this same volume Ernst M. Conradie provides support for the eschatological vision by affirming that "creation and redemption belong together." "On Responding to Human Suffering: A Critical Survey of Theological Contributions in Conversation with the Sciences," Ibid., 183.

Lecture Three

Extraterrestrial Life and Exotheology

We have been asking, where in the world is God? We began by asking: where we should go in formulating a conception of God in light of the challenges of atheism, pluralism, and Islam. Then we turned to evolutionary biology to ask: where do we see God's activity in the long struggle for species survival and the mechanism of natural selection? Now, we turn our gaze outward toward new apprehensions of our magnificent universe. Where do we see God amidst staggering distances and over deep time—perhaps 13.7 billion years of space-time—and amidst questions regarding the possibility of life on other planets?

Actually, the theory of evolution has appeared at the core of all three of our inquiries. The new breed of aggressive atheists relies on the theory of evolution, especially the apparent self-sufficiency of natural selection, to provide an explanation for life without recourse to divine intervention. The Darwinian model of evolution, as we saw in the second of our lectures, appears to favor only the victors in the struggle for survival; whereas the Christian understanding of God necessarily includes compassion for the losers. Now, in this third lecture, we observe that scientists who theorize about extraterrestrial life build their cases on the ideas of both cosmic evolution and biological evolution. Any engagement of contemporary science by Christian theology must be an engagement with evolution.

In what follows, I would like to introduce the task of *exotheology*, the theological analysis of questions rising from new knowledge about outer space. I also plan to address briefly what some deem to be challenges to the Christian faith raised by the prospect of contact with ETI.

Curiously, in our culture we find a myth at work. It is a single myth regarding extraterrestrial life, yet it comes to us in two overlapping forms. I will call it the *ETI myth* which comes to us in the standard scientific form plus the UFO form. In the scientific form of the ETI myth, reputable scientists speculate that extraterrestrial life exists, that it has evolved, and that in some cases it has evolved to a more advanced stage than we have on earth. In the form of the UFO myth, contactees and aficionados believe what the scientists believe; but they add that we have been visited by extraterrestrials. What is at work in both forms of this myth is the implicit belief that science has the power to save the nations of our world from self-destruction by nuclear war or eco-disaster or related violence. Both our respected scientists and the kookiest of UFO buffs interpret ETI through the same mythological lenses.

Let me clarify. The specific scientific question yet to be answered is this: does extraterrestrial intelligent life live somewhere else in the cosmos? This can be distinguished from the cultural question: what should we believe and hope for in light of the prospect of making contact with extraterrestrial life? The cultural question must confront the ETI myth.

When we turn to theological responses, I will ask whether people who have faith in God should believe the ETI myth. I will answer in the negative. The negative applies not to the question of whether extraterrestrial beings exist. Rather, it applies to the implicit belief that science can save earth's humanity from its own self-inflicted demise. Terrestrial science, even if augmented by extraterrestrial science, is insufficient for the human race to heal itself.

After making this point, I would like to give extended attention to a very old set of theological questions regarding redemption of extraterrestrial creation through Jesus Christ. Is one incarnation sufficient? Or, might redemption require multiple incarnations in multiple worlds? To deal with this set of issues, I will draw on the theological work of Paul Tillich, Wolfhart Pannenberg, and Karl Rahner. I will conclude that a single incarnation—the historical work of Jesus Christ—is cosmic in scope. No extraterrestrial, as far as a theologian can surmise, would be beyond the scope of God's saving grace.

Exotheology and Cosmotheology

Our inquiry here will be an exercise in what I call *exotheology*. With this term I refer to speculation on the theological significance of extraterrestrial life.[1] Actually the term 'exotheology', with the prefix 'ex' meaning outside, will permit the study of anything beyond our terrestrial domicile.

My label for this exercise, 'exotheology', is similar to one offered by Steven Dick. His term is *cosmotheology*. Whereas I tender somewhat cautiously the idea that the theologian can explore or speculate, Dick is ready to revolutionize the existing field of theology. "Cosmotheology, as I define it, means using our ever-growing knowledge of the universe to modify, expand, or change entirely our current theologies, whatever they may be. In short, cosmotheology takes into account what we know about the cosmos."[2] Dick is ready to throw out belief in the God of ancient Israel and substitute a new naturalism, a naturalism with God built into the universe. In my judgment, this is premature. So, even if the two terms are close enough to be interchangeable in some usages, I think I will stick with 'exotheology' and the more cautious connotations it has already garnered.

Astrobiology and the Prospect of Extraterrestrial Intelligent Life (ETI)

Our sister field in this inquiry will be astrobiology, in earlier times called exobiology or bioastronomy. Astrobiology is the scientific study of biological processes on earth, and beyond.[3] One of the most dazzling of the pioneers in this field is NASA's Christopher McKay, who has plans to terraform the planet Mars. He plans to seed Mars with oxygen emitting life forms. Once enough oxygen has been given off to create a new atmosphere on the red planet, then oxygen breathing life forms can be introduced. By this method life will spread from earth to the fourth planet. According to McKay, "Astrobiology has within it three broad questions that have deep philosophical as well as scientific import. These are the origin of life, the search for a second genesis of life, and the expansion of life beyond Earth."[4]

The first question overlaps with and incorporates the subject matter of evolutionary biology: how does life begin and develop? Darwin's model of evolution did not include the question of life's origin, only speciation. Astrobiologists seek the origin of life, whether on earth or anywhere else.

The answer to the second question—does life exist anywhere else in this universe?—is being pursued by SETI, which we will discuss shortly. From earth we scan the heavens for biosignatures, for evidence of an extraterrestrial genesis of life.

The third question is this: what is the future of life on earth and beyond? This includes forecasts of exporting life from earth to other locations in space; and it includes the interaction between life on earth and elsewhere. All three of these questions occupy today's astrobiologists.[5]

Our concern in this inquiry will be with the second genesis. Here astrobiologists search in space for astronomical conditions that could foster the development and emergence of life forms. They ask about the possibility that intelligent living creatures currently inhabit earthlike planets somewhere in the cosmos. To date no direct empirical evidence exists that ETI (extraterrestrial intelligence) exists. Despite more than three decades of active SETI (Search for Extraterrestrial Intelligence) research, no radio or microwave contact has occurred. OSETI (Optical Search for Extraterrestrial Intelligence), seeking biosignatures via laser detection, has similarly come up empty handed. If we rely solely on empirical evidence, then we have no reason to believe that anyone else is out there.

Space researchers are divided into two camps. The *Contact Optimists* contend that simple reasoning would suggest that the universe should be teeming with life. Those holding the *Uniqueness Hypothesis*, in contrast, suggest that the earth is probably the first and only home for a technological civilization. Those holding a rare-earth or unique-earth hypothesis usually concede that some form of life may have developed in some extrasolar locations. But the form of life is likely to be single-celled organisms or grasses or simple sea creatures like jellyfish. What they doubt is that the path of evolution would duplicate what has happened on earth, leading to the appearance of intelligence. Extraterrestrial life, maybe. Extraterrestrial intelligent life, no. The lack of direct empirical evidence to date seems to give the edge to the uniqueness hypothesis.[6]

Yet, contact optimists, like theologians, can speculate. And speculate they do. Today's star searchers can rely on a dramatic form of speculation known as the Drake equation. The *Drake Equation,* first formulated by Frank Drake in 1961 (National Radio Astronomy Observatory in Green Bank, West Virginia), looks like this:

$N = N^* f_p \, n_e \, f_1 \, f_i \, f_c \, f_L$

N^* = the number of stars in the Milky Way Galaxy

fp = the fraction of stars with planets around them

n_e = the number of planets per star

f_1 = the fraction of planets in n_e where life evolves

f_i = the fraction of f_1 where intelligent life evolves

f_c = the fraction of f_i that communicate

f_L = the fraction of the planet's life during which communication happens

N = the number of communicating civilizations in the galaxy.[7]

What star searchers gain from the Drake equation is not immediately the equivalent of N. Rather what they gain is a template, an open window to frame what we are looking at out there. As research advances new numbers can be plugged in. As we look beyond the Milky Way's 100 billion star systems, the scope expands enormously to 50 or maybe even 100 billion galaxies. The size of our universe is astronomical, to repeat a pun.

Well, if we are going to provide even a rough estimate of possible life bearing planets, what number should we use? Once we have examined the current state of our scientific knowledge and projected a reasonable estimate, George Coyne tenders that there are "10^{17} Earthlike planets in the universe."[8]

The nearly half century old Drake equation has been strictly speculation. The likelihood of actually discovering ETI seems to have increased since 1995, when the first planet was found around a star similar to our sun, 51 Pegasi. As technology increased to measure gravitational effects of suspected planets on their respective stars, so did the number of identified planets. These planets cannot be seen directly, but their gravitational pull can be detected by the wobble they cause on their star. Such evidence of perhaps two hundred forty extra-solar planets is now in. As one might expect, larger planets will likely be discovered first; and those already logged seem to be Jupiter sized objects orbiting quite close to their equivalent to our sun.

What we need, astrobiogists think, is a planet more earth size, metal rich, and sufficiently distant from its respective sun in order to provide liquid water.

To fit within the biophilic range, such a planet should be like the porridge Goldilocks preferred to eat, not too hot and not too cold. A Goldilocks planet would find itself in a Circumstellar Habitable Zone (CHZ). And such a planet would need to remain stable and safe for a long period of time, perhaps years numbered in the billions. To date, no empirical evidence that a Goldilocks planet exists is in; even though planet 581c orbiting a red dwarf star, discovered in 2007 by the European Southern Observatory in La Silla, Chile, comes close. Speculative considerations plus preliminary discoveries lead many astrobiologists to join the contact optimism camp.[9]

Here is how SETI's Frank Drake gives voice to speculations based on contact optimism. "Everything we know says there are other civilizations out there to be found. The discovery of such civilizations would enrich our civilization with valuable information about science, technology, and sociology. This information could directly improve our abilities to conserve and to deal with sociological problems—poverty for example. Cheap energy is another potential benefit of discovery, as are advancements in medicine."[10] Note how this optimism extends well beyond mere contact with ETI. It includes optimism regarding the solution to "sociological" problems such as poverty and energy while giving us a leap forward in medicine.

Evolution and the ETI Myth

Before drawing out the implications of astrobiological speculations for theology, let us follow a brief detour into the ETI myth regarding extraterrestrials. The Goldilocks assumption marks one way that science contributes to such a myth. As I have said, at work in contemporary culture is the *ETI myth*: the belief that extraterrestrial intelligent beings exist and, further, they are more advanced in evolution and technological progress. It is a belief without any direct empirical evidence. Yet it is such a potent belief that it structures research and interpretation of space phenomena. The ETI myth in its scientific form posits the existence of advanced ETI, while the UFO extension of the myth adds that ETI are visiting us.

Such a myth is a cultural construct, a window frame, so to speak, through which we look in order to view the world out there. In ancient times, myths were stories about how the gods had created the world in the beginning; and this beginning explains why things are the way they are in our contemporary experience. In the modern world, we think of ourselves as turning to science rather than myth to explain the origin of things. Yet, what ancient myth and modern science have in common is that they both provide a worldview, a frame for understanding and explaining what we experience. Or, to say it a bit more precisely, science contributes to the myths we modern people believe. At work in modern culture is an identifiable framework—a myth, if you will—within which we cast the questions we pose to the mysteries evoked by our experience with outer space.

What role does evolution play in this modern myth? Despite the controversy fueled by creationism and Intelligent Design, evolution has become so integrated into our culture that we all think from within an evolutionary paradigm. Evolutionary assumptions are everywhere at work. "Everything evolves," is a cardinal SETI doctrine.[11] A related assumption is at work: the more highly evolved, the higher the moral value. Social Darwinist Herbert Spencer based his ethics on this assumption. "The conduct to which we apply the name good, is the relatively more evolved conduct; and that bad is the name we apply to conduct which is relatively less evolved."[12]

Such evolutionary assumptions are being applied to the question of the existence of extraterrestrial life. Once evolution takes hold anywhere, moral progress is bound to advance. Here is one of the assumptions added by ETI myth believers: life must evolve wherever the conditions are right; and there simply must be extraterrestrial planets where this is possible. "Life is the product of deterministic forces," writes biologist Christian de Duve. "Life was bound to arise under the prevailing conditions, and it will arise similarly wherever and whenever the same conditions obtain. There is hardly any room for 'lucky accidents' in the gradual, multi-step process whereby life originated. This conclusion is compellingly enforced when one considers the development of life as a chemical process."[13] As long as the right chemical conditions exist somewhere in outer space—in the Goldilocks location— we can expect life to evolve and develop and progress. And, perhaps, some day we will meet this extraterrestrial life form. At the level of assumption, this evolutionary belief has worked its way into the ETI myth.

Christian de Duve speculates, based on the Green Bank equation of 1961 (see the Drake equation above) that "the figure of about one million 'habitable' planets per galaxy is considered not unreasonable. Even if this value were overestimated by several orders of magnitude, it would still add up to trillions of potential cradles for life. If my reading of the evidence is correct, this means that trillions of planets exist that have borne, bear, or will bear life. The universe is awash with life."[14] With such contact optimists speculating without empirical evidence that the universe is teeming with life, it is easy to imagine our culture developing images of just what that life might be like.

Nobel Laureate de Duve continues, feeding the myth with apparent scientific veracity. "My conclusion: We are not alone. Perhaps not every biosphere in the universe has evolved or will evolve thinking brains. But a significant subset of existing biospheres have achieved intelligence, or are on the way to it, some, perhaps in a form more advanced than our own."[15] When science becomes mythologized, we consider that our partners in outer space could be more highly evolved—"more advanced"—than we are.

Albert Harrison spells out what "more advanced" could mean. It means evolution into a state of international peace, beyond war. "A fundamentally positive picture emerges when we extrapolate from life on Earth: there are trends toward democracies, the end of war, and the evolution of supranational systems that impose order on individual nation-states. This suggests that our newfound neighbors will be peaceful, and this should affect our decision about how to respond to them."[16]

Carl Sagan similarly embraces the ETI myth, recognizing that it is based on speculation rather than sufficient empirical evidence to deem it to be scientific. "I would guess that the Universe is filled with beings far more intelligent, far more advanced than we are. But, of course, I might be wrong. Such a conclusion is at best based on a plausibility argument, derived from the numbers of planets, the ubiquity of organic matter, the immense timescales available for evolution, and so on. It is not a scientific demonstration."[17]

Paul Davies bends the ETI myth further in the direction of the UFO myth, by speculating about the spiritual superiority of our more advanced extraterrestrial colleagues. "It is clear that if we receive a message from an alien community, it will not have destroyed itself...it is overwhelmingly probable that the aliens concerned will be far more advanced than us....we can expect that if we receive a message, it will be from beings who are very advanced indeed in all respects, ranging from technology and social development to an understanding of nature and philosophy."[18] Davies proceeds to engage in theological speculation based upon his assumptions regarding extraterrestrial superiority due to their more advanced stage in evolution. "It is a sobering fact that we would be at a stage of spiritual development very inferior to that of almost all of our intelligent alien neighbors."[19]

These contact optimists have taken a number of non-empirical and speculative steps from the Drake equation to myth-like images of ETI more advanced in intelligence, in science, and even in spirituality. Might these more advanced intelligences represent our own future? And, if they would come to visit us, might they represent our own future coming to rescue us from taking the wrong evolutionary fork? Might an extraterrestrial science come to earth to supplement our own science and solve earth's problems? Might science in its extraterrestrial form become earth's savior? Such speculations rise up into the realm I refer to as "myth."

The Scientific Assumptions of the ETI Myth

The assumptions at work in the scientific form of the ETI myth presume the resolution of two competing interpretations of evolvability, one that supports earth's uniqueness and the other that supports contact optimism. The first interpretation emphasizes contingency and unpredictability. John Maynard Smith, for example, emphasizes the contingent and accidental appearance of the life forms we see on earth. Should evolution begin once again here or elsewhere, "there is no guarantee—indeed no likelihood—that the result would be the same."[20] In other words, the likelihood that evolution on an extraterrestrial planet would lead to intelligent life similar to our own is virtually nil. In contrast, Simon Conway Morris, argues that evolution follows a somewhat predictable track leading toward intelligent beings such as ourselves. "The emergence of human intelligence is a near-inevitability."[21] Morris bases his speculation on the history of convergence in earth's evolutionary past. "Convergence is ubiquitous, from molecules to social systems. In fact, the study of convergence reveals a deep structure to life. This strongly suggests that what is true on Earth is true anywhere....So, out there as and when we meet the aliens...the first will be bipedal and intelligent."[22]

We see here that among evolutionary theorists we can find two rather distinct views. One leads to the unique earth hypothesis, while the other to contact optimism. What seems to have occurred among scientists embracing the ETI myth is that they have sided with the second of these two options. The second option is just that, an option. It may be an attractive option; yet one cannot say that contact optimism has been decisively confirmed by the existing state of scientific knowledge.

What about the other option? What about the rare-earth or unique-earth hypothesis? Among scientists who are unsympathetic to the ETI myth we find evolutionary biologist, Francisco Ayala. When Ayala poses the question regarding the possible existence of ETI, he says, "My answer is an unequivocal 'no'." Why such a strong opposition to contact optimism? Because what has happened in our planet's evolutionary history has been contingent, not guided by an internal purpose or entelechy. Ayala argues that if we on earth were to replay "life's tape" from the beginning of life to the present, the course of evolution would not repeat itself. According to the existing evolutionary history, for the first two billion years only microbes existed on earth. The eukaryotes were the first organisms whose cells have a nucleus containing DNA; and, adds Ayala, there is nothing in the process that would make it likely that multicellular organisms would evolve. Evolution could have stopped right there. No animals might have come into existence. "We know that animals evolved only once. So, there is little likelihood that animals would arise again, if life's tape were replayed."

The phenomenon of extinction plays a big role in Ayala's argument. He notes that 99% of earth's species are now extinct. Five hundred thousand years ago most animal species had already become extinct; and their body plans would no longer be represented just one hundred million years later. Only one lineage gave rise to the vertebrates: animals with backbones, including fishes, amphibians, reptiles, birds and mammals. Even if the low probability event of the evolution of animals would be repeated, we have no reason to expect that animals with backbones would evolve. What follows is a virtually infinite improbability that primates would arise again, let alone hominids and *homo sapiens.*

In each chapter of the evolutionary story, we find a long concatenation of contingent if not unique events. We find millions of random mutations and environmental circumstances, all points where the history could have taken a different turn. The probability of a repeat of this history is so low as to be virtually nil. The evolutionary process would produce a different outcome every time it gets going.

Ayala would not find the Drake equation convincing, because the improbabilities of a repeat of our evolutionary progress are greater than the probabilities of communicating intelligent life coming into existence. If we "replay life's tape," the improbabilities get multiplied from year to year, from generation to generation, millions and millions of times. "The resulting improbabilities are of such magnitude that even if there would be millions of universes as large as the universe that we know, the products (improbability of humans x number of suitable planets) would not cancel out by many orders of magnitude. The improbabilities apply not only to *homo sapiens*, but also to 'intelligent organisms with which we could communicate'; by this phrase I mean organisms with a brain-like organ that would allow them to think and to communicate, and with senses somewhat like ours (seeing, hearing, touching, smelling, tasting) which would allow them to get information from the environment and to communicate intelligently with other organisms. We have to conclude that humans are alone in the immense universe and that we forever will be alone."[23] Such reasoning regarding contingencies in evolution lead Ernst Mayr, among others, to say that SETI is very likely to fail in achieving contact.[24]

Does Evolution Mean Progress?

With the earth uniqueness position before us, it becomes clear that SETI scientists and other contact optimists who believe in the ETI myth have bolstered their belief with assumptions regarding an inner drive or guide or *telos* within the evolutionary process. They assume that evolution and progress belong together. This is a decision regarding evolutionary theory, one that is not shared by all research biologists. This decision finds resonance in the wider culture, especially among those who have developed belief that UFOs can bring our planet salvation from a more highly evolved science and technology. To the UFO phenomenon we now turn.

Many research scientists are repelled at the prospect of comparing their assumptions with those of UFO believers, of course. They wish to protect pure science from pollution by pseudo-science and mass hysteria. Yet, we must proceed to place these two in tandem if we are going to understand just how the scientific mindset influences our culture. In what follows, we will not evangelize for belief in UFOs or in extraterrestrial visitation. Rather, we will study what people believe when they believe that UFOs come to us courtesy of extraterrestrial civilizations. What is significant is that the assumptions of both UFO aficionados and SETI researchers converge in the formation of a single worldview. This worldview is what I refer to with the term 'myth'. Exotheologians need to understand this myth as a myth, and interpret it accordingly.

Even if the UFO myth predated the current scientific version of the ETI myth, the latter is more conservative than the former. What the UFO myth adds is contact.

From the ETI Myth to the UFO Myth

I believe we can get at the structure of the mythological role extraterrestrials play in our culture by dissecting the UFO phenomenon, by examining the belief system surrounding the sighting of flying saucers.[25] As a phenomenon, what the UFO experience entails is a combination of objective appearance and subjective appropriation. To examine the UFO phenomenon is more than merely asking whether flying saucers are real or whether our earth is being visited by interplanetary travelers. It deals with what UFO witnesses perceive and how they interpret what they perceive. It deals with the entire UFO experience, from mere sighting to UFO research organizations to the establishment of UFO.[26]

Such an examination includes the belief system presupposed and developed by UFO experiencers and aficionados of the ETI idea. John Saliba puts it this way: "The meaning of the flying saucer phenomenon might lie more in its social and psychological dimensions than in whether extraterrestrials exist or not, or in what the aliens themselves are supposedly saying and doing. In other words, belief in flying saucers and alleged encounters with their occupants might reveal something important about human nature."[27] The questions regarding human nature prompted by the UFO phenomenon will be of interest to the theologian.

Whether a flying saucer report is a simple sighting of a daylight flying disc or a close encounter with an alleged alien being from an extraterrestrial world, the witness tries to explain the experience in terms of a worldview that makes sense. Curiously, the resulting explanation incorporates the theory of evolution combined with subtle religious symbolism. It goes like this. Life has developed on a distant earth-like planet and followed a path of evolution similar to our own. However, this alien life began earlier, and has had more time to evolve. Inherent in such evolution is progress. This means that the alien civilization in question has progressed further than we have. It is more advanced than ours. This is demonstrated because aliens have developed the technology for space communication or even space travel that we have not yet developed. In a sense, the space visitors are our own future coming back to visit us. And, if the space visitors bring their more advanced technology and perhaps even their more advanced spirituality, they can help us on earth heal our maladies. Extraterrestrials piloting flying saucers become celestial saviors.

Subtle religious symbolism becomes associated with the idea of evolutionary progress. Even though our word 'evolution' refers technically to speciation in biology, it becomes applied to progress in both technological and moral development. UFO experiencers routinely speculate: if aliens have developed space travel technology, perhaps they have developed a higher form of morality and politics. Evolutionary advance has become moral advance.

This speculation since World War Two has been tied specifically to the nuclear arms race, even if more recently concern over eco-catastrophe has been added. The logic goes like this: if our visiting aliens themselves went through a period of developing nuclear power and successfully avoided self-destruction, perhaps they can teach us on earth how to establish peace and avoid the threat of nuclear self-annihilation. What the space voyagers can bring to us is peace on earth, won through the advances of extraterrestrial science. Science, in its extraterrestrial and futuristic form, will become our savior.[28]

This UFO myth arose within a specific historical context, namely, the immediate period following World War Two when the world was trembling in fear over the nuclear arms race. This cold war anxiety included fear that political leaders were too inept to deal with the magnitude of the problem. Blinded by nationalism and jingoism, it was feared that one or another leader would hastily drop a bomb that would result in an uncontrollable retaliatory exchange. The result would be global self-destruction.

During the cold war, scientists were viewed as the only ones who could save the planet. We were proud of the genius of the scientists who invented the atomic bomb, who put an end to the Second World War. "Since the bomb exploded over Hiroshima, the prestige of science in the United States has mushroomed like an atomic cloud," wrote Martin Gardner in 1952.[29] Science represented power.

Science could also claim another virtue. The scientific community crossed national boundaries. Scientists communicated with one another regardless of national loyalties. Could a confederacy of scientists representing different nations do what political leaders could not by themselves do, namely, provide an institution for arms control? Could these broad-minded geniuses overcome their narrow-minded political leaders and provide a single planetary policy that would maintain world peace?

Or, to put it another way, could terrestrial scientists save us? No. Why? Because they vacillated too much between nationalism and internationalism. Even if a select group of high minded scientists could dedicate themselves to world peace, there would always be that minority of Frankensteinian mad scientists who would sell their souls to the interests of their well paying governments. On the one hand, the scientific community seemed to hold the power to save. On the other hand, scientists were feared because they, like other mortals, could be swayed and bribed by national interests to perpetuate the spiraling competition for nuclear superiority.

This love-fear tension in the relationship between science and culture is aptly reflected in the career of Atomic Bomb maker, J. Robert Oppenheimer. "The physicists have known sin; and this is a knowledge which they cannot lose," wrote Oppenheimer in 1948 in *Technology Review* and *Time* magazine.[30] Once Pandora's Box had been opened and nuclear weapons knowledge began spreading, Oppenheimer sought to slam the lid down again through internationalizing atomic oversight. He proposed in the *New York Times*

Magazine "that *in the field of atomic energy* there be set up a world government. That *in this field* there be a renunciation of sovereignty....to protect the world against the use of atomic weapons and provide it with the benefits of atomic energy."[31] He pressed his case in the White House and the United Nations. His efforts failed. Then President Harry Truman led America into the dizzying arms race of the cold war. Science, despite its knowledge and power, could not save us.

Kai Bird and Martin Sherwin comment, "After Einstein, Oppenheimer was undoubtedly the most renowned scientist in the country—and this at a time when scientists were suddenly regarded as paragons of wisdom. His advice was eagerly sought in and out of government." Oppenheimer's advice was sought, but not taken. Citing Freeman Dyson, Bird and Sherwin aver that Oppenheimer tried to become "the savior of humanity at the same time."[32] However, this attempt at terrestrial salvation through science failed. Could an extraterrestrial science accomplish it? Enter: the UFO myth.

The Day the Earth Stood Still

Oppenheimer's failing press for international arms control was launched in 1948. By 1951 the first of the authentic flying saucer movies had made it to the silver screen, *The Day the Earth Stood Still.* In this classic film, a flying saucer lands on the grassy mall near the White House in Washington. Its pilot is an extraterrestrial, Klaatu. He has come to earth to negotiate with the heads of state of every nation. This issue is serious and urgent. Unless earth cease and desist its development of rocket propelled atomic weapons, Klaatu's confederacy will have to eliminate us before we can become a threat to them.

Klaatu fails to convince our political leaders. In fact, myopic political leaders will not even give him a hearing. Only scientists take the celestial diplomat seriously. Klaatu explains to an aging physicist, Professor Barnhart, that the aliens fear further development on earth of what is now only a "rudimentary" form of atomic weaponry. Up until this point the interplanetary confederation had not concerned itself with wars on earth, because earth's inhabitants had not yet evolved to the point of being able to affect the extraterrestrials. Killing one another on earth with primitive guns and tanks would elicit no extraterrestrial notice. But now, that atomic weapons could be tied to rockets and shot into outer space, human violence could spill into the extraterrestrial domain. Klaatu's mission is to warn earthlings of the dire consequences. And, only earth's scientists, not its politicians, could understand this warning and take the appropriate preventative action.

In the concluding scene on site of the flying saucer, the space visitor, Klaatu, makes a speech. "The universe grows smaller every day, and the threat of aggression by any group anywhere can no longer be tolerated. There must be security for all or no one is secure. Now this does not mean giving up any freedom, except the freedom to act irresponsibly. Your ancestors knew this when they made laws to govern themselves and hired policemen to enforce them. We of the other planets have long accepted this principle We have an organization for the mutual protection of all planets and for the complete elimination of aggression. The result is we live in peace, without arms or armies, secure in the knowledge that we are free from aggression and war, free to pursue more profitable enterprises." Note how this extraterrestrial confederacy has evolved beyond where we have. They have progressed to a stage in evolution where war is no more. Peace prevails. The extraterrestrials bring peace as an option for Planet Earth. We terrestrials can choose either peace or obliteration. What the extraterrestrials bring is scientific advance combined with moral advance. This is the foundation of the UFO myth.

Even gad as primary, *The Day the Earth Stood Still*, was fiction, it became important in two regards. First, it vividly reflected the cultural ambiguity regarding the double valence of science, namely, science as destroyer and science as savior. Second, it fed the growing cultural understanding of the potential significance of ETI. The UFO cults and political movements of the later 1950s all incorporated Klaatu's speech, sometimes adding layers of mysticism to the movie's otherwise terse reliance on the scientific mindset.

UFO cults from the 1950s to the present day embrace various levels of the UFO myth, complete with alleged evolutionary advance and scientific rescue from nuclear self-destruction. On November 20, 1952, George Adamski claims a flying saucer descended to greet him in the California desert. A man from Venus emerged from the craft to carry on a telepathic conversation. The countenance of the Venusian visitor had the innocence of a child combined with a grave sense of wisdom and love. Donned with a single weave garment and long hair blowing in the breeze, he had a near Jesus-like appearance. With his hands the Venusian drew the picture of a mushroom shaped cloud and said, "boom! boom!" He warned that nuclear arms testing was not only dangerous for life on earth, but radio active contamination could spread to other planets. Despite this stern warning, he spoke with compassionate understanding. "His expression was one of understanding, and great compassion; as one would have toward a much loved child who had erred through ignorance and lack of understanding." The space emissary's mission was "to help us and perhaps protect us from ourselves."[33]

Among today's UFO religious organizations, the International Raëlian Movement (IRM), numbering about 60,000 in membership, may be the largest. In an alleged 1973 revelation to Claude Vorilhon, who then became renamed Raël, an extraterrestrial visitor warned earthlings of the dangers of nuclear testing and weaponry. "You urgently need to stop nuclear weapons testing…and if you become a threat to us, we will…have to reduce you to silence."[34] Commenting on Raël's space teachers, Susan Palmer says that they "do not confine themselves to ethical and theological matters. They have a great deal to say about the use of science to solve the world's problems. Science poses the ultimate threat to our well-being and survival, but it also offers the solution to this threat, and the key to immortality and a materialistic salvation."[35]

I am not alone among scholars who try to piece together cultural anxiety over science and technology with the development of the ETI myth along with its partner, the UFO myth. Diana Tumminia describes the UFO myth as a postmodern phenomenon: "Postmodern myths, such as flying saucers, extraterrestrial deities, and alien abductions, express pluralistic collage-like symbolism of relatively recent origin. With the dawning of the rational technological age, social scientists expected secularization and science to wipe out superstition and magical religions. This has not happened. Instead, a magical enchanted worldview subverted the scientific paradigm into an animistic account of space being that was readily available for our mass consumption. That condition now pervades in our popular culture."[36] Note that in her description, Tumminia suggests that the UFO myth subverts the scientific paradigm by reintroducing magic. This is debatable; yet, I do not want to debate this issue here. Rather, I would like to point out that when we look at the ETI myth as believed by SETI scientists, we see no obvious magic. We see only science in a very speculative form. It is not the return of magic that defines the ETI myth or even its UFO variant; rather, it is the belief that salvation comes to earth from the heavens, from outer space.

In summary, the UFO myth begins with the assumption that science is savior. But, because earthly science has "known sin" by letting loose the nuclear arms race and putting the entire planet at risk, only a terrestrial science augmented by an extraterrestrial science can accomplish salvation. Salvation will come in the form of world peace. Extraterrestrials are able to do for us what we almost but not quite can do for ourselves, namely, establish security through a system of global arms control. Perhaps the more highly evolved UFOnauts can save us from destroying ourselves.

Can We Compare Science with UFOs and Religion?

Now, one might object to my line of reasoning saying, the UFO myth has nothing to do with science! Why compare let alone conflate these two? Albert Harrison might put up such an objection. He writes, "SETI is not to be confused with religion and myth, so any superficial similarities among extraterrestrial radioastronomers, God, ancient astronauts, and space brothers have to be taken with a huge grain of salt."[37] Now, just what is the difference? Harrison answers, "God, if He exists, is supernatural. Extraterrestrials would be the product of biological evolution."[38] Yes, of course this marks a significant difference, a metaphysical difference. Yet, at what Harrison calls the "superficial" level I believe we need to acknowledge what both SETI and the UFO myth hold in common: they both take the theory of evolution and project it onto the heavens with no empirical evidence that ETI even exists. What both the science of astrobiology and UFO believers share is a wider culture with an evolutionary worldview. This worldview is extra-scientific, because the genuinely scientific model of evolution expunges the doctrine of progress. Both SETI and UFO belief embrace an extra-scientific concept of evolution replete with progress built-in.

And, in the case of the ETI myth, the ego of terrestrial science is so puffed up as to project an imaginary extraterrestrial science coming to earth to save us from self-destruction. What terrestrial science has been unable to do—bring peace on earth—will soon be accomplished by extraterrestrial angels wearing white lab coats.

What we are doing here is trying to identify the shared mindset that gives rise to astrobiology, SETI, and UFO belief. The term 'myth' is the most appropriate term to identify what is happening here.

Myth and Theology

When it comes to theological discernment, one must first ask the question: does myth count in theology? No. Most theologians are willing to interpret myths, but certainly not willing to believe them in their literal form. Myths tell us about human anxieties and propensities and speculations, to be sure; but they do not tell us about the reality of God. This applies to the UFO myth or ETI myth as well. It is the task of the theologian to say: don't believe this myth. Science cannot save us from self-destruction, whether it be terrestrial or extraterrestrial science.[39]

Science, just like all other human enterprises, is fallen. Science, like everything else the human race touches becomes contaminated by sin, by our exploitative propensity to use anything at our disposal to defeat our competition, survive, and triumph. Despite the marvels of the new knowledge gained and new technology produced, science has become subject to the funding of jingoists and the ambitions of militarists. Advances in scientific knowledge lead frequently to equal advances in the breadth and efficiency of murder, mayhem, and mass destruction. Each decade marks a new level of global terror due to advances in nuclear and biochemical weaponry. This spiral is beyond political control, religious control, moral control, and beyond self-control. If the UFO myth suggests that augmenting terrestrial science with extraterrestrial science will provide this control, the theologian must simply shrug and say: where is the evidence for such a belief?

The blind alley into which the myth leads us I call the 'eschatological problem'.[40] The myth proposes that if we in our generation simply make the right choice that, with the advance of science, we in the human race can advance from warring destruction to a state of world peace. Yet, the skeptical theologian should ask: how do we get from here to there? Can a leopard change its spots so easily? If science got us into the present mess, how can we expect science to liberate us from this mess? If we have evolved to this point, why should we think that more evolving will save us?

Salvific healing, according to the Christian theologian, comes from divine grace granted us within the setting of our fallen life on earth. The cross and resurrection of Jesus Christ symbolize the presence of this saving grace. In the cross we see God's identification with the victims of human violence. In the resurrection we see God's promise that we will not forever be locked into the spiral of violence. When trusting this promise, Christians believe that the Easter resurrection of Jesus is the herald announcing a new and qualitatively different future. It will be God's final future. It will be the equivalent of a new creation in which crying, and pain, and suffering, and the threat of such will be no more. What God has promised in the Easter Christ is healing, eschatological cosmic healing. Unambiguous healing—even world peace—will come to us only as an eschatological transformation, as an act of God.

Standard Theological Challenges

Returning now to astrobiology, what are the theological implications? The standard answer to those who look at terrestrial religion from the outside is this: if we gain conclusive knowledge that we are not alone in the universe, this will shatter all current religious belief systems. Allegedly, ancient beliefs in the God of Israel and other beliefs in personal gods will be crushed under the weight of new cosmic knowledge. Why does it appear that our religious traditions are so fragile? Because, allegedly, our inherited religious traditions are terrestrial, earthbound, parochial, narrow, and atavistic. This is quite a set of assumptions, but we find them at work in many quarters.

One of America's founding fathers, Thomas Paine, launched this argument in 1793. "Though it is not a direct article of the Christian system that this world that we inhabit is the whole of the habitable creation," he wrote; "yet it is so worked up therewith from what is called the Mosaic account of the Creation, the story of Eve and the apple, and the counterpart of that story—the death of the Son of God, that to believe otherwise, that is, to believe that God created a plurality of worlds at least as numerous as what we call stars, renders the Christian system of faith at once a little ridiculous....The two beliefs cannot be held together in the same mind; and he who thinks that he believes in both has thought but little of either."[41] The logic seems to go like this: once we speculate about life on other planets, then the Christian faith looks ridiculous. Once we make contact, the Christian faith will collapse.

That was two centuries ago. We find the same set of assumptions at work today; but, what is added, is the theory of evolution. Everything evolves, many assume, even religion. So, we can predict that the ancient religions we have inherited will evolve in the future. And the shock of contact with ETI will hasten that evolution.

This is the logic of SETI scientist, Jill Tarter, who constructs an entire scenario based upon the Drake equation. Although to date no contact of any sort with extra-terrestrial intelligent life has occurred, Tarter can imagine myriads of planets teeming with living beings. All will have evolved. And, if some got a start earlier than we on earth, they will have evolved further. Their technology will have progressed; and they may even have a technology sufficiently advanced to communicate with us. Further, she imagines that these extra-terrestrial societies will have achieved a high degree of social harmony so as to support this advanced technology. And, still further, if they have developed their own religion, it too will be more advanced than the religions we have on earth. Or, more likely, the "long-lived extraterrestrials either never had, or have outgrown, organized religion."[42] We can forecast, then, that contact between earth and ETI will necessitate either the end of our inherited religious traditions or a new incorporation of universal worldview.

Steven Dick makes the same evolutionary assumptions and foresees virtually the same scenario. Earth's ancient beliefs in a supernatural personal god just must go by the wayside. To take its place will be belief in a new God, a naturalist's God, built right into the universe. Dick welcomes the arrival of "the concept of a natural God—a God *in* the universe rather than outside it."[43]

Now, in my judgment, such anti-Christian and anti-terrestrial religious speculation is unnecessary; and it is misleading. It commits the fallacy of false alternatives: either believe in the ancient God of Israel or believe the ETI myth. This is a false set of alternatives, because theologians both Christian and Jewish could easily absorb new knowledge regarding the existence of extraterrestrial life. Both Christians and Jews have debated the theological implications of many worlds since the middle ages, with increased interest during the post-Reformation and post-Copernican periods. Among major contemporary theologians, only a few address the issue of ETI, but those who do are quite comfortable at integrating possible new knowledge on the subject.[44]

Yes, of course, we can find recalcitrants who fit the atavistic paradigm. Maverick Orthodox theologian Seraphim Rose rejects both ETI and evolution. The Orthodox Christian knows that "man is not to 'evolve' into something 'higher', nor has he any reason to believe that there are 'highly evolved' beings on other planets."[45] Creationist Jonathan Sarfati makes the same judgment, but with a touch less confidence. "It was on Earth that the first human couple rebelled against its creator and brought the cosmos under His curse. Thus it would have affected Martians, Vulcans, Klingons and any other being in the universe. The second person of the holy trinity incarnated on Earth alone, took on human nature, died for the sins of those with whom He was the kinsman redeemer relationship, then ascended to the right hand of God the Father. He did not take on Vulcan or Klingon nature, and He will have only one bride—the church—for all eternity. It would therefore seem hard to reconcile intelligent life on other worlds with the doctrine of the incarnation. It would also seem odd for God to create microscopic life on other planets, but we should not be dogmatic on this."[46] Yes, such arguments can be heard. Still, the number who hold this position is relatively small. And in this second instance, note the caution against being too "dogmatic on this."

"Attempts to reconcile Christian revelation with extraterrestrials abound," writes skeptic Benjamin D. Wiker.[47] When we turn to the leading figures in theology, openness to ETI is certainly the order of the day. Karl Rahner, the twentieth century giant of Roman Catholic theology, argued that on the planets strewn throughout the cosmos we could expect separate but significant "histories of freedom."[48] Evangelical leader, Billy Graham, said in 1976, "I firmly believe there are intelligent beings like us far away in space who worship God....But we would have nothing to fear from these people. Like us, they are God's creation."[49] I see no reason to think of the Christian faith as fragile in the face of possible new knowledge about space neighbors.

Multiple Incarnations?

One curious question arose already in the middle ages and is being asked again in our own era: if ETI inhabit their own worlds, would each world receive its own incarnation of Christ? Is the single redemptive event we know as the divine incarnation complete with crucifixion and resurrection on earth salvific for life forms elsewhere in the cosmos? Or, must the redemptive act take place repeatedly, once for each intelligent species?[50]

This question arises both within established theological conversation and outside, where antagonists would like to challenge the coherency of Christian theology. Thommaso Campanella (1568-1634), when defending Galileo in *Apologia pro Galileo*, speculated: "If the inhabitants which may be in other stars are men, they did not originate from Adam and are not infected by his sin. Nor do these inhabitants need redemption, unless they have committed some other sin."[51] What we see here is multiple speculations. Might ETI have sinned in parallel fashion to what has happened here on earth? If so, would they need their own event of salvation, or would they benefit from what has happened in our world? Does the theology of incarnation depend on the presence of sin and the need for redemption, or is incarnation a natural extension of God's work in creation? What would happen to the personhood of Christ should we posit multiple incarnations? As long as no ETI shows up on our doorstep, the sense of urgency to address such questions is light.

Whether urgent or not, we might try to draw up some parameters for pursuing such questions further. Perhaps we should do so in response to the challenge of possible contact with ETI. University of Singapore philosopher, Roland Puccetti, poses just this challenge.

Puccetti begins by asking whether ETI would be considered persons. Yes, he answers. According to Puccetti, "despite secondary biological differences they [extra-terrestrial intelligent beings] would certainly qualify for person-status, since they would be both capable of assimilating a conceptual scheme and the sort of entity to which one can quite reasonably ascribe feelings. Since these are…the essential requirements for constituting a moral agent, to say that extraterrestrials are persons is the same as to say they are moral agents."[52]

Having established the personhood of ETI, Puccetti then does a push-me pull-you number on Christian theology. On the one hand, he argues that multiple incarnations ought to be expected. On the other hand, he tries to show that the concept of person in incarnational theology lacks coherence. "Except on the extreme kenotic view—that between His Incarnation and Ascension the Son of God more or less lost His divine attributes and was temporarily nothing *but* man—Christianity has no conclusive theological reasons for opposing multiple incarnations in which non-human rational corporeal beings would have their natures hypostatically united to that of the same Son of God."[53] Putting himself into the place of a Christian theologian, which he is not, Pucetti argues that if no change in the Godhead is involved in Christ's earthly incarnation, and if what Christ does is take human nature up into the divine life, then it would follow that this could be done multiple times, each with a different life form. If two natures, one finite and the other infinite, are compatible in one person, then why not several times on different planets?

Then, like a battleship firing its sixteen inch cannons, Puccetti blasts away with the big numbers. He elects to use 10^{18} for the number of likely life bearing planets in the universe. The incarnate Son of God would be a corporeal person, to be sure; and this means he could be only one place at one time. Yet, the number of places to visit would be overwhelming. "There would be on the order of 680,000,000 to 3,400,000,000 incarnations occurring simultaneously from now to the extinction of life on all such stars. Allowing for earlier incarnations reduces this figure a bit, but not enough to make any real difference."[54] The impression the reader gets is that this would be absurd. The numbers are too big. The concept of an incarnate person seems to collapse under its own incoherence.

Puccetti gloats that he has won a victory in his attack on religion. "What I have been trying to do...is to show how a correct analysis of the person-concept combined with the not unreasonable belief in extraterrestrial natural persons actually undermines belief in God."[55]

Ernan McMullin finds it ironic that Puccetti demands that corporeality be included in his concept of person. The Latin term, *persona*, from which we derive 'person' in its modern usage, originally applied to the three persons of the divine Trinity. The concept did not originate in reference to corporeal beings. McMullin goes on to identify some shaky presuppositions in the Puccetti argument, one of which is a warning about relying on big numbers. The Drake equation is strictly speculative, not empirical. "One has to be wary here of a fallacy induced by the contemplation of large numbers....It is one thing to discover one or a small number of ETI sites based on the interpretation of incoming radiation. It is another thing entirely to establish, on the basis of a theoretical analysis of the multiplicity of processes involved in the appearance and survival of intelligent life, that the number of centers of such life in the universe is of a certain order or even that it is, in very general terms, extremely large."[56] McMullin does not believe this is a slam dunk refutation of Puccetti, even if he has reduced the force of Puccetti's argument. We still need to sort out the issues surrounding the meaning of incarnation on other planets.

Paul Tillich and Extraterrestrial Incarnation

In his influential *Systematic Theology,* Paul Tillich addresses directly the question of the efficacy of redemption on earth for life on other planets. How should we "understand the meaning of the symbol 'Christ' in the light of the immensity of the universe, the heliocentric system of planets, the infinitely small part of the universe which man and his history constitute, and the possibility of other 'worlds' in which divine self-manifestations may appear and be received....The function of the bearer of the New Being is not only to save individuals and to transform man's historical existence but to renew the universe....The basic answer to these questions is given in the concept of essential man appearing in a personal life under the conditions of existential estrangement. This restricts the expectation of the Christ to historical mankind."[57]

Having affirmed here the efficacy of redemptive action by God in Jesus Christ, Tillich speculates about additional possibilities. "At the same time, our basic answer leaves the universe open for possible divine manifestations in other areas or periods of being. Such possibilities cannot be denied.... Incarnation is unique for the special group in which it happens, but not unique in the sense that other singular incarnations for other unique worlds are excluded."[58] Multiple incarnations would be reasonable to Tillich, even though to date we have no proof that such a thing has happened.

Tillich goes on to speculate that ETI might be in a situation similar to our selves here on earth. They might be fallen, what Tillich calls "estranged" from God. Even in their estranged situation, however, God as the ground of their being would be at work with reconciling love. "If there are non-human 'worlds' in which existential estrangement is not only real—as it is in the whole universe—but in which there is also a type of awareness of this estrangement, such worlds cannot be without the operation of saving power within them.…The expectation of the Messiah as the bearer of the New Being presupposes that 'God loves the universe', even though in the appearance of the Christ he actualizes this love for historical man alone."[59]

It is not clear here whether Tillich would consider ETI as persons in the sense that Puccetti does. Tillich uses the term "non-human." Yet, Tillich considers the possibility of estrangement and awareness of estrangement, which would put them into the category or moral agents. So, perhaps with Tillich, ETI would be non-human persons. And, because Jesus the Christ appeared for historical human persons, an additional incarnation for these non-human persons would be in order.

Yet, Tillich does not need to follow the trail to this destination. Such an incarnation would not be necessary, given Tillich's assumption that God's creative presence and grace is available throughout the creation. All Tillich really needs to affirm is that God's saving work would be present, regardless of whether in incarnate or some other form.

Wolfhart Pannenberg and Cosmic Presence

The position Wolfhart Pannenberg takes is similar to that of Tillich, even though Pannenberg is less likely to consider the option of multiple incarnations. Both theologians agree that God's redemptive as well as creative work would be present in other worlds, but Pannenberg comes closer to saying that the saving work of Jesus Christ on earth is efficacious for the entire universe. "It is hard to see…why the discovery of nonterrestrial intelligent beings should be shattering to Christian teaching. If there were such discoveries, they would, of course, pose the task of defining theologically the relation of such beings to the Logos incarnate in Jesus of Nazareth, and therefore to us. But the as yet problematic and vague possibility of their existence in no way affects the credibility of the Christian teaching that in Jesus of Nazareth the Logos who works throughout the universe became a man and thus gave to humanity and its history a key function in giving to all creation its unity and destiny."[60]

Pannenberg can express confidence in the universal efficacy of Jesus Christ because his incarnation is the incarnation of the universal Logos, the principle by which all of creation is generated and held together. Like thoughts originating in our mind, the Logos originated in God. And as our thoughts come to expression in speech, when God speaks the Son becomes differentiated from the Father; and the world with all of its particularity comes into existence. This is the divine nature of the Son, the universal ground of all finite reality.

We are stepping back from redemption to the doctrine of creation here. Pannenberg associates creation with the Trinity, not with the Father alone. It is through the Son as the Logos that the existence of the entire finite creation is wrought. "If the Logos is the generative principle of all the finite reality that involves the difference of one thing from another—a principle grounded in the self-distinction of the eternal Son from the Father—then with the advent of ever new forms differing from what has gone before there comes a system of relations between finite phenomena and also between these phenomena and their origin in the infinity of God. As the productive principle of diversity the Logos is the origin of each individual creature in its distinctiveness and of a the order of relations between the creatures."[61] Note that the Logos establishes both individuality and the relations between individuals. Perhaps this is the condition that makes it possible for the Logos to become a single individual, Jesus of Nazareth, while still expressing universal finite reality.

Because each and every personal life on another planet would have been created through the same divine Logos, one need not assume a lack of connection between what happens on earth and what happens in even the furthest reach of outer space. The temporal and spatial finitude of Jesus of Nazareth distinguishes him as an individual when set next to all other sentient beings either on earth or elsewhere. One need not postulate some special metaphysical track that each species of intelligent beings would follow, warranting their own incarnation. In Tillich's words, the incarnation in Jesus is the "concrete universal."[62]

Karl Rahner: Incarnation as God's Perfecting of Nature

We could fantasize about ETI. We could imagine that they are better than we are. In C.S. Lewis' novels, *Out of the Silent Planet* and *Perelandra,* he could imagine a race of people who had not fallen into sin. Many of today's scientists and UFO true believers fantasize that ETI are more virtuous than we are, because they are more highly evolved. Until we meet them, of course, we simply will not know for certain.

Robert John Russell, in contrast, predicts that, most likely, ETI will find themselves in the same situation of ambiguity that we find ourselves. "I predict that when we finally make contact with life in the universe…it will be a lot like us: seeking the good, beset by failures, and open to the grace of forgiveness and new life that God offers all God's creatures, here or way out there."[63]

Now, with this in mind, let us ask a question internal to theology: what warrants incarnation? Had Adam and Eve not fallen, would the Son of God still appear in incarnate form? Is it the world's fallenness that creates the need for redemption? Or, might the incarnation be due strictly to God's self-communication in creation? Tillich seems to assume that our situation of estrangement calls out for an incarnate visitor from the ground of being. Fallenness calls out for redemption. Pannenberg, in contrast, makes the incarnation independent of the fall. "The incarnation cannot be an external appendix to creation nor a mere reaction of the Creator to Adam's sin."[64] God's presence in Jesus Christ adds the grace of redemption upon the grace of creation. The latter is a completion of the former.

Be that as it may, in the minds of most Christian theologians incarnation and redemption seem to belong together. The church long remembers Athanasius (296-373) saying of Jesus Christ, "He was made man that we might be made God."[65] Eastern Christians both ancient and contemporary hold that in the incarnation Jesus Christ recapitulated all that is human, healed it, and set us on a course toward deification, *theosis*. Such deification had been God's original plan in creation, to be sure; but because of human sinfulness God found it necessary to take redemptive action. "The Fall demands a change, not in God's goal, but in His means," writes Vladimir Lossky; "For the atonement made necessary by our sins is not an end but a means, the means to the only real goal: deification."[66]

In contrast, as we just saw in Pannenberg, some Western theologians have argued that incarnation was destined due to the internal dynamics of the Trinitarian life. Bonaventure (1221-1274), for example, rejected the idea of the incarnation in Christ as some sort of afterthought, a way to fix what was broken. Incarnation was willed by God for its own sake, not for the sake of a lesser good. In addition. said Bonaventure, God's entry into the created realm as a human serves to unite all of creation with humanity. The incarnate Christ serves to perfect nature. All of God's creative work is a form of incarnate self-expression.

For Karl Rahner, the incarnation in Jesus Christ is God's self-communication. "The world and its history are from the outset based on the absolute will of God to communicate himself radically to the world. In this self-communication and in its climax (i.e., in the Incarnation), the world becomes the history of God himself."[67] On the one hand, through the incarnation God actualizes our human potential. On the other hand, we human beings and all of creation get taken up into God's own history. "The incarnation of God is therefore the unique, *supreme*, case of the total actualization of human reality…God has taken on a human nature, because it is essentially ready and adoptable…and comes therein to the fulfillment of its own incomprehensible meaning."[68] This understanding of incarnation is one of adding grace upon grace.

If we were to try to construct a theological opinion regarding extraterrestrials—an opinion that could be significantly revised once we meet them—we might extrapolate from this understanding of incarnation perfecting creation. After weighing the merits of the alternatives, I surmise that those who argue for an incarnation based upon a further expression of God's original creative grace have the stronger position. I further suggest that the historic events surrounding Jesus of Nazareth count significantly if not decisively for what will eventually become the single convergent history of the cosmos as a whole.

Summary

This lecture has been an exploration in exotheology. Actually, exotheology is by definition an exploratory discipline, a speculation on the theological implications of possible contact with extraterrestrial intelligent beings.

We have distinguished between the raw core of astrobiology's search for a second genesis, on the one hand, and the cultural overlays of the ETI myth, on the other. What we find in the ETI myth is a complex speculation that projects a repeat of earth's evolutionary history stretched out by the doctrine of progress so that ETI are imagined as beings more highly evolved than we, more advanced, and superior not only in science but in morality. These projections are most satisfying to terrestrial scientists because they paint a picture of science as our world's savior, revealing the hidden religious dimensions built into scientific speculation. The UFO form of the myth makes this explicit as it paints pictures of ETI coming to our planet to rescue us from self-destruction by means of extraterrestrial augments to terrerstrial science. My theological recommendation is that we avoid believing this myth, even if it is touted by the most respected of scientists in our society.

The ETI myth does not warrant confident belief for three reasons. First, the history of science on earth has been ambiguous. Even though science has brought us modern medicine which saves lives, it has brought us the atomic bomb and the terror of the nuclear arms race. No precedent exists that science on its own can heal itself and become benign let alone salvific. Second, the theory of evolution as currently employed by biologists and astrobiologists resists the doctrine of progress. There is no built-in principle of advance. At most, one can find reason to affirm growth in complexity within biological evolution, but definitely not something we might wish to call "advance." The idea of progress over time is an ideological import into the theory. So, to paint a picture of ETI as more advanced in science and morality is to speculate well beyond the limits of even what the theory of evolution would permit. Third, as of yet no empirical evidence for the existence of ETI exists. Yes, that evidence may appear in the future. At that moment when we actually encounter ETI, however, we may be in for some surprises. ETI might be quite different than we expect. All this leads us to treat the ETI myth with caution, not rejecting it out of hand but recognizing that its plausibility hangs on a very thin thread.

When it comes to the centuries old debate within Christian theology regarding life on other worlds, we need to sift out two issues. The first is the question of whether Christian theology could absorb new knowledge regarding neighbors living in other star systems. Those who contend that the Christian worldview is too brittle or too fragile to adapt to this new knowledge underestimate the degree of adaptation that has already taken place. The theory that the Christian religion would collapse when shocked by ETI has insufficient evidence to support it.

Second, internal to theological history, the persistent issue has been whether the redeeming work of Jesus Christ would require multiple incarnations or just one. Arguments for both have been raised. I have contended: if we think of the creation of the entire universe in Trinitarian terms, the divine grace through the second person of the Trinity is already omnipresent with all of reality, with even the most distant of galaxies. This would tend to favor the sufficiency of a single incarnation, the historical event of Jesus Christ on earth. Yet, arguments for multiple incarnations due to the need for redemption from possible fallenness have some merit. In either case, we should think of the incarnation in Jesus Christ as well as any others as grace perfecting nature, as grace upon grace.

Where in the World is God?

The immensity of our expanding universe and the prospect of intelligent life appearing on planets very distant from our earth makes us ask: where in the world is God? The God revealed to us in ancient Israel and in the cross of Jesus Christ is, first of all, *beyond.* The creator of this universe with all of its immensity and grandeur is even more immense and more grand. Out of love, this God brought all that is from nothing into being; and God continues to attend to every moment on every planet in every galaxy. God is beyond while, at the same time, *intimate* to sentient consciousness within the humblest corners of this creation. God is present to the innermost dimensions of each self, more present to you and me than we are to ourselves. This paradoxical tension between God as beyond and God as intimate never ceases.

God also appears to us in the form of promise. In Romans 8:21-23, we find Paul telling us: "For the creation was subjected to futility, not of its own will but by the will of the one who subjected it, in hope that the creation itself will be set free from its bondage to decay and will obtain the freedom of the glory of the children of God. We know that the whole creation has been groaning in labor pains until now; and not only the creation, but we ourselves, who have the first fruits of the Spirit, groan inwardly while we wait for adoption, the redemption of our bodies." We find God in the promise that the future will not be like the long evolutionary past we have inherited. The future will bring healing, peace, love, and life eternal. Where is God? God is in this promise.

Notes

[1] See: Ted Peters, *Science, Theology, and Ethics* (Aldershot UK: Ashgate, 2003) 121.

[2] Steven Dick, "Cosmotheology: Theological Implications of the New Universe," in *Many Worlds: The New Universe, Extraterrestrial Life and the Theological Implications,* edited by Steven Dick (Philadelphis and London: Templeton Foundation Press, 2000) 200.

[3] http://scienceandreligion.arizona.edu/project.html

[4] Christopher McKay, "Astrobiology: The Search for Life Beyond the Earth," in *Many Worlds*, 45. The "second genesis" might turn out to be the first and "original genesis." The discovery of carbon-containing molecules composed of six to eleven atoms each elsewhere in the Milky Way suggests a readiness for life on a broad scale. "The discovery of biologically significant molecules in interstellar clouds of gas and dust could push life's history much farther back in time and out into space." Kathryn Garfield, "Did Life Begin in Space?" *Discover* (November 2006) 16.

[5] See: Albert A. Harrison, *Starstruck: Cosmic Visions in Science, Religion, and Folklore* (New York and Oxford: Berghan Books, 2007) 42.

[6] Glen David Brin, "The Great Silence: the Controversy Concerning Extraterrestrial Intelligent Life," Quarterly Journal of the *Royal Astronomical Society* 24 (1983) 283-309.

[7] For the Drake Equation see: http://www.activemind.com/Mysterious/Topics/SETI/drake_equation.html.

[8] George V. Coyne, S.J., "The Evolution of Intelligent Life on Earth and Possibly Elsewhere: Reflections from a Religious Tradition," in *Many Worlds*, 180.

[9] What would be needed to see an earth-sized extrasolar planet would be a telescope allowing scientists to see wavelength 1×10^{-10} times fainter than the star it orbits. Diffracted starlight must be suppressed to see the earth-like planet. This could be accomplished with telescopes located in space. John T. Trauger and Wesley A. Traub, "A laboratory demonstration of the capability to image an Earth-like extrasolar planet," *Nature* 446: 7137 (12 April 2007) 771-773. Essential to life is liquid water; yet, the mere presence of water is not enough. Too much absorption of stellar electromagnetic radiation can limit if not eliminate the possibility of life, as can too little. See: John Raven, "Photosynthesis in watercolours," *Nature* 448:7152 (26 July 2007) 418. The interaction between a planet's sun and its water needs to be just right. It also needs a variant of the Goldilocks range.

[10] Cited by Diane Richards, "Interview with Dr. Frank Drake," *SETI Institute news,* 12:1 (First Quarter 2003) 5.

[11] Edna Devore, "Voyages Through Time," *SETI Institute News,* 12:1 (First Quarter 2003) 7.

[12] Herbert Spencer, *The Data of Ethics* (New York: A.L. Burt Company, 1879) 28-29.

[13] Christian de Duve, *Vital Dust: The Origin and Evolution of Life on Earth* (New York: Basic Books, 1995) xv.

[14] Ibid., 121.

[15] Ibid., 297.

[16] Albert R. Harrison, *After Contact: The Human Response to Extraterrestrial Life* (New

York and London: Plenum Press, 1997) 312.

17 Carl Sagan, *Pale Blue Dot: A Vision of the Human Future in Space* (New York: Random House, 1994) 33. Sagan speculates not only about the scientific advances of ETI, but also wonders what might happen if visiting ETI would find human beings delicious to eat. "Why transport large numbers of us to alien restaurants? The freightage is enormous. Wouldn't it be better just to steal a few humans, sequence our amino acids or whatever else is the source of our delectability, and then just synthesize the identical food product from scratch?" Ibid., 353. Sagan developed his own science based atheism, a view quite similar to that of Richard Dawkins. SETI scientist Seth Shostak observes, "Sagan is sharpening the logical tools he wields to address the matter of God's existence. How plausible is the premise? How convincing is the evidence?" "Carl Sagan andt he Science of God," *Discover* (November 2006) 69. It seems these "logical tools" apply more strictly to the question of God's existence than to the question of ETI's existence.

18 Paul Davies, *Are We Alone? Implications of the Discovery of Extraterrestrial Life?* (New York: Penguin Books, 1995) 32-33

19 Ibid., 33.

20 John Maynard Smith, "Taking a Chance on Evolution," *New York Review of Books* (14 May 1992) 34.

21 Simon Conway Morris, *Life's Solution: Inevitable Humans in a Lonely Universe* (Cambridge: Cambridge University Press, 2003). xii. Even with this premise, environmental conditions restricting the likelihood of a Goldilocks planet means, "life may be a universal principle, but we can still be alone." Ibid., 105.

22 Simon Conway Morris, "Not So Alien," *SETI Institute News,* 12:1 (First Quarter 2003) 10-11.

23 Quotes here taken from Francisco J. Ayala, "The Evolution of Life on Earth and the Uniqueness of Humankind." in: S. Moriggi and E. Sindoni, eds., *Perché esiste qualcosa invece di nulla? (Why There Is Something rather than Nothing?)* (ITACAlibri: Castel Bolognese, Italy, 2004), 57-77.

24 Ernst Mayr, "Can SETI Succeed? Not Likely," http:www.planetary.org/explore/topics/search_for_life/seti/seti_debate.html. On this SETI website Carl Sagan argues for an "Abundance of Life-Bearing Planets." Ibid.

25 We need to distinguish sharply between the UFO phenomenon and science fiction. They are not the same. They rarely overlap. Their respective articulations of cultural sensibilities differ. In the 1950s, science fiction lifted up the cold war by describing interstellar aliens as hostile enemies to be defeated, on the model of the struggle between the West and the Soviet Union. In contrast, the growing number of UFO believers viewed extraterrestrial aliens as neutral if not benevolent visitors who could save us on planet earth from self-destruction. Only two major movies offered an authentic presentation of the UFO phenomenon, *The Day the Earth Stood Still* (1951) and *Close Encounters of the Third Kind* (1977).

26 As of this writing the most interesting of recent daylight disc sightings took place over Gate C-17 at O'Hare International Airport at 4:30 pm, November 13, 2006. Sighted by United Airline pilots from two different planes as well as ground personnel, one of the two dozen witnesses described the "metallic disc" as "a

rotating Frisbee." After it ascended at high speed, it left a round hole in the 1900 foot cloud cover so that blue sky could be seen through it. See: Sam Maranto, "Incident at O'Hare," *MUFON UFO Journal* 466 (February 2007) 3-5.

27 John A. Saliba, "UFO Contactee Phenomena from a Sociopsychological Perspective: A Review," *The Gods Have Landed: New Religions from Other Worlds*, edited by James R. Lewis (Albany NY: SUNY, 1995) 241.

28 See: Ted Peters, *UFOs—God's Chariots? Flying Saucers in Politics, Science, and Religion* (Louisville: Westminster John Knox Press, 1976).

29 Martin Gardner, *Fads and Fallacies in the Name of Science* (New York: Dover, 1952, 1957) 3. Gardner analyzes the UFO phenomenon, dismissing it as hysteria. What Gardner does not recognize is the cultural connection between UFO beliefs, evolution, and the prestige of science.

30 Kai Bird and Martin J. Sherwin, *American Prometheus: The Triumpth and Tragedy of J. Robert Oppenheimer* (New York: Random House, Vintage Books, 2005) 388.

31 Ibid., 347.

32 Ibid., 390.

33 George Adamski and Desmond Leslie, *Flying Saucers Have Landed* (New York: Abelard-Schuman, 1955) 198.

34 Raël, *The True Face of God* (Quebec: The Raëlian Foundation, 1998) 94-95.

35 Susan J. Palmer, *Aliens: Raël's UFO Religion* (New Brunswick NJ and London: Rutgers University Press, 2004) 24. Conservative Christian groups such as *Reasons to Believe* tend to reject UFO contactee claims, especially if they have occult trappings, as most do. The UFO theologies are perceived as competitors to classic Christian teaching. "Often the metaphysical messages and revelations given by contactees directly deny and contradict historic Christian doctrines about God, Christ, sin, salvation, and Scripture....they deny the cosmic Lord and resurrected Savior of the world....As a whole, the religious nature of the contactee experience reveals a fundamentally different worldview than that of historic Christian theism. As always, one would do well to heed the warnings of Scripture: "Dear friends, do not believe every spirit, but test the spirits to see whether they are from God" (1 John 4:1). "Test everything. Hold on to the good" (1 Thess. 5:21). Test everything; even the existence of little, green men. Keneth R. Samples, "Alien Encounters Fail the Test," http://www.reasons.org/resources/fff/2001issue06/index.shtm, accessed 2/3/07.

36 Diana Tumminia, "From Rumor to Postmodern Myth: A Sociological Study of the Transformation of Flying Saucer Rumor," *Encyclopedic Sourcebook of UFO Religions*, edited by James R. Lewis (Amherst NY: Prometheus Books, 2003) 103.

37 Harrison, *Starstruck*, 99.

38 Ibid.

39 Not just theologians are critical here; some scientists also caution us against thinking of science as savior. John Holdren, President of the American Association for the Advancement of Science told those assembled at the 2007 annual meeting in San Francisco, "I'm a great believer in science and technology, but the notion that science and technology will ride to the rescue is a pernicious one....Believing in technological miracles is usually a mistake." Cited by Robert Coontz, "Wedging

Sustainability Into Public Consciousness," *Science* 315:5815 (23 February 2007) 1068.

40 See: Ted Peters, *Futures—Human and Divine* (Louisville KY: Westminster John Knox Press, 1977).

41 Thomas Paine, *The Age of Reason* (Buffalo: Prometheus Books, 1984) 52.

42 Jill Cornell Tarter, "SETI and the Religions of the Universe," in *Many Worlds*, 146.

43 Dick, "Cosmotheology," 202. "The effect on non-Adamist religions would be less than on those that teach salvation through a single God-head." "Extraterrestrial Life," in *Encylcopedia of Science and Religion,* edited by J. Wentzel Vrede van Huyssteen, 2 volumes (New York: Macmillan, 2003) 1:318.

44 "If Christian theology takes seriously its confession that God created the universe, then it ought to welcome any and all new knowledge about the universe—including the possible verification of extraterrestrial life," writes Mark Worthing. "The Possibility of Extraterrestrial Intelligence as Theological Thought Experiment," in *God, Life, Intelligence, and the Universe,* ed. by Terence J. Kelly, S.J., and Hilary D. Regan (Adelaide: ATF Press, 2002) 71. Rational debate over the existence and relevance of extraterrestrial beings has imbued Christian theology since the middle ages; and it continued right down into the modern era of astronomy. "The extent of the debate is suggested by the fact that, by 1916, more than 140 books (not counting works of science fiction) and thousands of articles addressing this issue had already appeared.…Not least surprising is the fact that authors found ways to marshal extraterrestrials in support of, or in opposition to, Christianity, deism, atheism, and dozens of other creeds and philosophies." Michael J. Crowe, "The Plurality of Worlds and Extraterrestrial Life," *The History of Science and Religion in the Western Tradition: An Encyclopedia*, ed. by Gary B. Ferngren (New York and London: Garland Publishing, 2000) 343.

45 Fr. Seraphim Rose, *Orthodoxy and the Religion of the Future* (Platina CA: Saint Herman of Alaska Brotherhood, 2004) 114. Rose does not speak for Orthodoxy regarding ETI. A much more revered and followed Orthodox theologian, Vladimir Lossky, has argued that the existence of other planets bearing life is not precluded from reading Genesis or the ancient church fathers. *The Mystical Theology of the Eastern Church* (London: James Clarke, 1957) 106.

46 Jonathan D. Sarfati, "Bible Leaves No Room for Extraterrestrial Life," *Science and Theology News*, 4:7 (March 2004) 5.

47 Benjamin D. Wiker, "Alien Ideas Christianity and the Search for Extraterrestrial Life," http:crisismagazine.com/november2002/feature7.htm, accessed 2/3/07.

48 Karl Rahner, *Foundations of Christian Faith* (New York: Crossroad, 1978) 446.

49 *National Enquirer* (November 30, 1976).

50 Denis Edwards, for example, would argue for multiple incarnations. "One should "not rule out the possibility of extraterrestrial incarnations and economies of salvation," he writes. "Extraterrestrial Life and Jesus Christ," *Pacific Journal of Theology and Science,* 1:1 (2000) 19. Mark Worthing, in contrast, argues that "if there is other intelligent life in the universe then God relates to it through Christ—the same Christ through whom God reconciles us to Godself. I do not believe Christian theology can posit a multiplicity of Christs and remain Christian theology." "Possibility of Extraterrestrial Intelligence," 83.

[51] Cited in Michael J. Crow, *The Extraterrestrial Life Debate 1750-1900: The Idea of a Plurality of Worlds from Kant to Lowell* (Cambridge and New York: Cambridge University Press, 1986)12.

[52] Roland Puccetti, *Persons: A Study of Possible Moral Agents in the Universe* (New York: Herder and Herder, 1969) 106.

[53] Ibid., 136.

[54] Ibid., 139.

[55] Ibid., 143.

[56] Ernan McMullin, "Life and Intelligence Far From Earth: Formulating Theological Issues" in *Many Worlds,* 167.

[57] Paul Tillich, *Systematic Theology* (3 Volumes: Chicago: University of Chicago Press, 1951-1963) 2:95.

[58] Ibid., 96.

[59] Ibid.

[60] Pannenberg, *Systematic Theology,* 2:76.

[61] Ibid., 62.

[62] Brother Guy Consolmagno would concur. "Even though the life of Jesus occurred at a specific space-time point, on a particular world line (to put it in general relativity terms), it also was an event that John's Gospel describes as occurring in the beginning-the one point that is simultaneous in all world lines, and so present in all time and in all space. Thus, there can only be one Incarnation--though various ET civilizations may or may not have experienced that Incarnation in the same way that Earth did." "Would You Baptize an Extraterrestrial?" http://www.beliefnet.com/story/35/story_3519.html, accessed 2/3/07.

[63] Robert John Russell, "What Are Extraterrestrials Really Like?" in *God for the 21st Century,* edited by Russell Stannard (Philadelphia and London: Templeton Foundation Press, 2000) 66.

[64] Pannenberg, *Systematic Theology*, 2:64.

[65] Athanasius, *Incarnation of the Word*, §54.

[66] Vladimir Lossky, *Orthodox Theology: An Introduction* (Crestwood NY: St. Vladimir's Seminary Press, 1989) 110-111.

[67] Karl Rahner, "Christology within an Evolutionary View of the World," *Theological Investigations*, 22 vols. (London: Darton, Longman & Todd, 1961-76; New York: Seabury, 1974-76; New York: Crossroad, 1976-88) V:186.

[68] Karl Rahner, "On the Theology of the Incarnatio

HOMILY

A religious service on Sunday morning is part of the conference. Attendance is voluntary. The service is planned and led by a retired Mennonite pastor, which means that it is based on the simplicity of Mennonite worship.

Traditionally the homily, presented by one of the participants in the conference, is a part of the proceedings.

REMARKS ON THE RELATIONSHIP BETWEEN RELIGION AND SCIENCE

by

Joseph A. Bracken, S.J.

Xavier University, Cincinnati, Ohio

The alleged perennial conflict between the claims of science and classical Christian belief is, as John Hedley Brooke and others have conclusively established, largely a myth unwarranted by the facts in each case. Those who for their own reasons resent what they see as the intrusion of Church authorities into their domain of science, however, are often more than willing to perpetuate this myth even in the absence of real evidence. To take the most famous conflict-case, historical research reveals that Galileo lacked adequate empirical confirmation for his own heliocentric hypothesis and thus should have been content to put it forth simply as a working hypothesis rather than as established scientific fact. In this way he would have been able to counter on scientific grounds the geocentric theory of Tycho Brahe, the most celebrated astronomer of his day, and at the same time satisfy Vatican authorities that he was not thereby subverting the authority of the Bible. So the condemnation of his views by the Catholic Church and his subsequent house arrest never had to happen if he had been both a better scientist and a more politically astute son of the Church.

But at least one other classical Christian belief still seems to stand in direct opposition to contemporary natural science. The Bible predicts a fiery end of the world and then a "new creation" in which the saved will enjoy the presence of God forever and the damned will suffer the just penalty for their sins. Professional cosmologists, on the contrary, claim that life on this planet will presumably end long before the universe as a whole either undergoes a "big crunch" or a "deep freeze" followed perhaps by a new "big bang" and a new cosmic epoch. How is one to reconcile such conflicting approaches to the future for humanity?

In my view, we should take a cue from the Galileo case and first acknowledge basic differences in methodology for religion and science and then take careful note of the multi-dimensional character of reality, the way in which different levels of explanation are needed to explain the world in which we live. John Haught in recent publications has made this point clear when he points to the fact that even within the natural sciences there are different levels of explanation, each with its own distinctive methodology. One does not use the formulas of quantum mechanics to solve problems in chemistry or biology. Both of these disciplines have their own methodologies and operational principles which would in turn be of little or no value for analysis of the quantum level within Nature. Theology, accordingly, should have its own resources and its own methodology to solve its own problems, dealing with the meaning and purpose of human existence in our contemporary world. As Galileo already noted in the 17th century, the Bible teaches us how to go to heaven, not how the heavens go. So there should be a distinctively religious approach to the issue of the end of the world which should not be in conflict with scientific or philosophical cosmology. But, if this is the case, what should be such a religious approach to the End-Time?

Here I find a recent article by the Australian theologian Denis Edwards in the academic journal *Theological Studies* to be of considerable value. Edwards begins by claiming that the Christian doctrines of creation, redemption and the Last Judgment are intimately interconnected. Relying on the theology of Duns Scotus rather than on that of his 13th century contemporary Thomas Aquinas, Edwards claims that the Son of God did not become human primarily to redeem us from our sins but rather to share the divine life with us. The self-giving love of the triune God, in other words, brought it about that one of the divine persons became human both to lead human beings out of their sinfulness and, even more importantly, to introduce their creatures to the joys of the divine life both in a partial way here and now and in its fullness after death. Hence, the resurrection of Jesus is a symbol of what is in store for the entire human race in due time. Jesus during his lifetime responded with total self-giving love to the Father's wishes, and the Father in a return of self-giving love shared the fullness of divine life with his divine-human Son when the Son's life on earth was ended. So it will be for all of us as we pass from this life into eternal life at the moment of death. This life, accordingly, is for all of us a slow process of divinization which will reach its climax only when we die and fully surrender our lives to God after the example of Jesus on the cross.

Denis Edward's vision of the goal of the Christian life is certainly inspiring to ordinary Christians. But is it plausible to those trained in the natural sciences or is it so foreign to their professional experience as to seem like a pious fairy tale? Here I would argue that an intermediary between classical Christian belief in eternal life and the findings of natural science is needed to render the Christian vision rationally plausible for those not already predisposed to accept that belief as true. Such an intermediary should logically be a philosophical world view that makes good sense to both believers and non-believers. Such a commonly accepted world view, of course, does not yet exist. The situation in which we in the modern era find ourselves is in this respect notably different from the situation of Aquinas, Duns Scotus and other medieval thinkers. They used the philosophy of Plato and Aristotle to ground both their understanding of the world of Nature and their interpretation of God's Word as recorded in the Bible. But the philosophy of Plato and Aristotle no longer seems to work as a world view suitable for both scientists and Christian believers. Too many unanswered questions remain for both groups.

In his article Edwards relies heavily on the work of Karl Rahner, one of the major Christian theologians of the last century. But Rahner himself over the course of a long career seems to have moved away from classical Thomism to a more experience-based Neo-Thomism. Yet even here questions remain. How can God, for example, both exist apart from the world and yet be the "horizon" or ontological ground of the cosmic process as Rahner himself believed in virtue of his reinterpretation of the philosophy of Martin Heidegger? How can God truly be involved in an interpersonal relation with us human beings and yet in line with Neo-Thomism still be unchanging Being, the Pure Act of Existence? My own approach to these issues has been consciously to mediate between the classical metaphysics of Being and a neo-classical metaphysics of Becoming in the hope that a more process-oriented approach to reality might stand a better chance of being accepted as plausible by those in the natural and social sciences. But what would this imply?

First of all, scientists must be more open to question their own philosophical presuppositions about what they are dealing with in their research. Saying, for example, that matter is convertible with energy is only a start. What then is energy and where does it come from so as to produce our radically interconnected world? Still another question: are natural processes nothing more than the sum total of their functioning parts? Or are these processes, while clearly emergent from the dynamic interplay of their parts, governed by different laws and new properties, so as to constitute something other than those same parts?

Turning to Christian theologians, I pose other questions. Should they too be moving toward a new metaphysics, perhaps one based on universal intersubjectivity and relationality, in order to explain the God-world relationship and in particular the Christian doctrines of creation, redemption and Last Judgment? If, for example, the three divine persons are understood to be an ongoing community of interrelated subjects of experience, then they presumably deal with all their creatures on an intersubjective basis as likewise subjects of experience. That is, at least most of the time they use persuasion rather than coercion to influence the moment by moment decisions of their creatures. Thus, on the one hand, the divine persons can positively influence what happens in this world without suspending the laws of Nature and, on the other hand, human beings and to a lesser degree all other creatures through their ongoing decisions can share with the divine persons in a common life. Further details of such an intersubjective approach to the God-world relationship are available in books and articles that I have written over the years. So let me end by giving you just one further hint as to how such a "conversation" between the divine persons and all their creatures could take place.

When human beings enter into conversation with one another and thus set up over time an interpersonal relationship, they end up creating an intentional "space" between themselves which is progressively structured by what they say and do with respect to one another. Why could not such a "space" likewise exist between the divine persons and all their creatures which would be structured by all the events of history, above all, by the events of Salvation History as recorded in the Bible? Furthermore, is this not basically what we mean by the Biblical term the Kingdom of God? The Kingdom of God, to be sure, will reach its full fruition only in eternity. How then can we human beings and all other creatures in this world of space and time be incorporated into the purely spiritual world of the Kingdom of God? If one grants that we are here and now subjects of experience in dialogue with the divine persons as likewise subjects of experience, then even now we are living a truly spiritual life. Right now, of course, we have to communicate with one another in various material ways (through words, gestures, actions). But in eternity, when we are no longer bound by the limiting conditions of space and time, we will presumably have more directly spiritual ways to communicate with one another. This fits quite nicely, incidentally, with Alfred North Whitehead's proposal many years ago that actual entities or momentary subjects of experience are the final real things of which this world is made up, even though further refinement is needed to convert Whitehead's philosophy into a full metaphysics of intersubjectivity such as I have in mind here. But that is a task to talk about some other time.

Discussions

Discussions form a major part of the Conference. After listening to the Speaker's primary ideas presented in lecture, participants engage the Speaker in conversation centered on those ideas. These discussions are monitored to provide all who have questions or wish to make comments the opportunity to do so.

This section is organized according to topics discussed. Within each topic the individual questions, comments, and responses are organized chronologically. Individual questions or comments are edited, sometimes severely, in order to preserve the essence of the question or comment. Ted Peters' responses are edited only when I believe that improves sentence structure. It has been my intent to preserve the flavor of Ted Peters' interaction with the group.

Individuals asking questions or making comments are not identified by name. An individual is identified by discipline, profession, or level of study, such as seminary, when that is helpful in understanding the source of the question or comment.

Topics

1. Atheism
   - a) Religion as Dangerous
   - b) God in the Equations
   - c) History of Religion
   - d) God as Primary Cause
   - e) Contingency and Chance
   - f) God Hypothesis
   - g) Atheist Lapses
2. Ethics
   - a) Cultural leaps
   - b) Human Ethical Response
   - c) Spirituality and Race Relations

3. Extraterrestrials
    a).Character of UFO Communities
    b).Multiple Incarnations
    c).Faith and Redemptive Violence
    d).Evolution and Doctrine of Progress
4. Religion
    a)Resurrection and the New Creation
    b)Mormon Addition to Genesis
    c)Sanctification and Christian Growth
5. Religion and Science Dialogue
    a).Religion as Biologically Based
    b).Pluralism Origins and Ideas
    c).Talking Without Quarreling
    d).Murphy and Lakatos
    e).Spectrum of Thought
6. Science
    a).Reductionism and God Talk
    b).Contingency and Release
    c).DNA as the Language of God
    d).DNA as Instruction Manual
    e).Physics of Immortality
    f).Equations as Pointers
    g).Anthropic Principle
    h).Analogies and Lack of Data
    i).Salvation, Lifespan, and Repentance
    j).Promethean Myth
7. Sin
    a).Murder and Chimpanzees
    b).Murder, Empathy and Suffering
    c).Pollution and Guilt
    d) Genesis and Genetics
    e) Genesis, Evolution, and Empathy of God
    f) Embarrassment, Shame and Guilt
    g) Genetic Heritage and Jesus
    h) Salvation and Condemnation

8. Sociobiology
   a) Conflict within the Genotype
   b) Race and Gang Wars
   c) Gang Wars and Cultural Damage
   d) Selfish Gene, Wilderness and Yawning
9. Trinity
   a) Basic Concept
   b) Jesus' Relation to the Father
   c) Rational Mind

1. Atheism

a) Religion as Dangerous

Question: We may contend that religion is not dangerous. But I think that thinly veiled condescension or one-dimensionalization is dangerous. I believe your presentation of movements such as pluralism has been unfair. I welcome your response.

Peters: Let me see if I understand what you are saying. Are you saying that religion is really dangerous and I underplayed it, or you are saying that by citing these people as saying that religion is dangerous that I overstated the case? I'm not sure that I understand what you are saying.

Question [continued]: You were trying to present the position held by those you called evangelical atheists as a claim that religion is dangerous. Although we may claim that religion is not dangerous, we cannot claim that condescension and generalization are not dangerous as well. I sensed condescension in the first part of your lecture.

Peters: Well, I may still be failing to understand you, and I'm sorry if that is the case. I am trying to imagine myself in the shoes of Dawkins and Harris, like the rest of us, seeing suicide bombings. And these suicide bombings are the products of schools where these young people go and are taught these religious doctrines that lead them to do these violent acts. And so from their point of view, if that is religion, then that is really a bad thing. That's what they think.

Let me just say that there is a certain logic to it. Now, the Muslims that I hang around with would never want to become suicide bombers. In fact they would like to practice *Tawhid* [a term used to emphasize the unitary nature of God] and reverence for God who is one. And they are Muslims, too. So let me just say that I think the experience with Islamic religion, which is the one that is on everybody's mind these days, is clearly ambiguous in character. And one probably could come up with double experiences in certain chapters of the history of Christianity as well. But at any rate, I'm trying to understand what they are saying. I think that their analysis is mistaken. But I'm not sure what you are saying, and I'd like to understand it better.

Question [continued]: I think that some of the simplifying phrases you used in your lecture, such as "an atheist would say," or "a pluralist would say," oversimplify. And I think your representation of Muslim science overlooked a rich tradition.

Peters: I'm just trying to work through complicated things to try to understand. So I say, well, "A Muslim would say…" I'm just trying to sort of report what I perceive to be the internal logic of Islamic thinking. So I don't think of it democratically, that if you had a thousand Muslims 823 would say this and a minority would say that. I'm not thinking of it that way. I'm trying to capture what I believe would be the coherent line of thinking within Islamic thought when I say those kinds of things.

b) God in the Equations

Question: I do not believe that a scientist can really be an atheist. The terms we use represent part of a continuum that we do not understand. It seems that the atheist is too focused on the finite.

Peters: If Richard Dawkins were here and he were to say, "Professor, I've looked for God in the equations and I can't find God there," what would you say?

Question [continued]: You'd better look at your equations again. He is there.

When I talked about Christian apologetics at my church, I kept missing something until I realized that the real apologetics is personal, as in St. Paul's epistles. When I switched to the personal I began gaining ground, because no one could counter my experience.

Peters: Well, I've been thinking a lot lately about why it is that religious people in general, and Christians in particular, talk about God in personal ways. I think about Francis Collins praying. He probably prays in personal language, "God our Father" or something like that. Scientists, when doing research, don't use personal language or personal concepts. They use impersonal language. And philosophy, which preceded science, also was impersonal in character. Yet the Bible is very personal in most respects. The Bible is very personal in character.

So I wonder if part of where we find ourselves in the modern world is that we are living with our religious language, which is symbolic and personal in character, and then we are trying to integrate that with the impersonal language and concepts of science. It's a little bit like oil and water. It's not impossible. But if we did find God in the equations, would we address that God in prayer? I suspect maybe not. I don't know.

c) History of Religion

Question: Dawkins and others are extreme fundamentalist atheists. There is a vast middle ground of persuadable atheists. The concept of God has in general evolved incrementally. The conversation with atheists might follow the same course. Could you comment on this?

Peters: Tell me, in this scenario, what role does atheism play in your question? Is the atheism methodological in the sense that we are going to look at the history of the phenomenon of religion to try to see what its origins might be? And in this are we going to be objective and scientific, rather than theological about it? Is that what the atheism refers to? Or do you mean an ideological atheism of the type that Dawkins would have?

Question [continued]: No, I'm thinking of the methodological. When we speak of special revelation the person listening hears that as ideological, not as methodological.

Peters: Let me give you a rather lengthy answer to that.

When I got into the field of science and religion, I studied at the University of Chicago under Langdon Gilkey. Gilkey held the two language position: science speaks one language while religion speaks another. Yet, Gilkey could also point out that science imbues Enlightenment culture. Our culture has been scientized, so to speak. But I also studied the history of religions and became enamored of Mercia Eliade. There is a lot of knowledge about religion as culture available here. When I put Gilkey and Eliade together, I could see that our culture of science plays the same role that religion played in archaic cultures.

Frankly those people who advance the theory that religion is a product of evolution don't seem to have studied religion. They have a very truncated view. And Richard Dawkins would be the worst case of this very truncated view. If Dawkins would study Eliade, he would see that a lot of knowledge exists about religious sensibilities across cultures and across eras. Gilkey along with Eliade provide a rich and thick approach if we want to understand *homo religioso*, the human being as having a religious disposition. And if those who are advancing this theory about religion's evolution would begin with the existing knowledge about religion, and then ask if it has biological origins, I would have a great deal more respect for it than I currently do. That doesn't mean that the theory is wrong. I am just saying that we have a long way to go before they persuade me that this is a sufficient explanation.

Suppose they do persuade me that religion has evolved. That's fine. Then you've got two more things to take into account. One is the axial breakthrough. It is very possible that the human race is developing what scholars used to call primitive religious sensibilities and symbol systems. We've got records and we know what all that looked like, namely, projections of every day human experience on to an imagined world of the gods. The gods of archaic religions looked like us, basically. But then you get to the first millennium B.C. and, according to Karl Jaspers along with Eric Voegelin and others of this school of thought, you see a sudden onset of transcendental insights. The breakthrough to transcendence happens in Greece; it happens in India; it happens in different places in the world. And suddenly the human consciousness is shocked by recognizing its own finitude and its own limitedness over against a nameless transcendent which comes to us from beyond. Well, that's not going to be accounted for in a reductionist evolutionary a theory. What we inherit in Judaism and Christianity is special revelation that is actually within the context of the axial breakthrough.

There's a second is a point I would like to add. I like the neo-orthodox theologians quite a bit. The neo-orthodox theologians have a low opinion of religion. This is because they had seen religion baptize the German war machine. They had seen religion baptize European colonialism and expansion. So, they didn't like religion very much, even their own religion. In fact, their opinion of the church was kind of low. The prophetic element within Christianity became quite strong in this school of thought. They would emphasize that we've got to have a relationship with God, and that relationship with God stands in judgment over against church, society, culture, etc. Only an appeal to the transcendent God of the axial breakthrough can provide the distance necessary to critique our culture, our scientized culture. The attempt to reduce religion to an evolved cultural phenomenon is an attempt to eliminate the prophetic critique of science. It is an attempt to treat religion as if the transcendent does not exist.

What happens, I think, for the religious consciousness in the wake of the axial breakthrough, in the wake of what we are calling special revelation, is that we have this double relationship to the natural world and to the historical world. On the one hand, it's the only world we can live in. On the other hand, the reality of God transcends it and judges it. I don't know how an evolutionary theory could account for that dimension. And so for these reasons I'm kind of a spectator watching to see how that evolutionary theory of religion develops. And if it is confirmed, it will be kind of interesting. But I'm not sure that it will affect the core of my faith.

d) God as Primary Cause

Question [philosopher]: I haven't read Dawkins book, *The God Delusion*, and so what he means by finding God in the equations, I'm not exactly sure.

I'm also not sure whether Dawkins has a worked out epistemology or not. But I'm going to at least put one in his mouth.

Last night and again here you have spoken of God as a personal reality known in personal ways. But theism is far more than just asserting a personal reality. It's also asserting an ontological dependence of the cosmos on God's being. It's an ontological relationship and not merely a personal one. And it's also a causal relationship. Of course our Catholic friends would perhaps chime in to help us distinguish between primary and secondary causation. But at least at the primary level it's a causal one. And so at that level and thinking about it that way, Dawkins' questions make a lot more sense than just saying, "You look into your equations, what did you expect to see?" "You went out to the desert, what were you looking for?" Your daughter is putting around the day care, what did you expect to see? What were you looking for?

A lot of scientists and physicists particularly have a pragmatist epistemology. What difference does it make for the world that proposition A is true or false? Or if God exists and God is what theism says God is? Or if God is not just a personal reality, but also the ontological ground of all being. Or the causal origin and, one might say, the ultimate cause in the sense of the final cause of all things, the Alpha and the Omega in that sense. Or if God is not just the beginning at any point of time but as origin and final consummation of all things. Then what difference does that make for the way the world works?

It doesn't make any difference. And it may not be a variable or a constant in your equation. But it may be some other feature of your equations.

Newton, for example, thought the omnipresence of God was to be found in the absoluteness of space as the necessary presupposition of his physics. Now, it turns out he was wrong about absolute space, or at least we think he was wrong about that. But at least he thought it made a difference, and not just a god-of-the-gaps sort of thing, "Well, if God's presence isn't there the solar system falls apart, the center doesn't hold."

Not that, but as an underlying presupposition of the mathematical intelligibility of nature. It is not necessarily that you look into your equations and exclaim, "Oh! There's the God factor right there, what value do you plug-in for that?" But it is the question of what difference does it make for the cosmos if the proposition is true? And I don't know if Dawkins would subscribe to a pragmatist theory of truth, but at a practical level he probably does, as I would think most scientists would.

Peters: Thanks for that. That was very eloquent and very insightful. You don't need to read Dawkins, you really understand the issues very well. Actually, the phrase "finding God in the equations" is one that I use as a sort of shorthand for what I think are the issues. I think it does appear in his book, but he doesn't use it to the extent that I do. It's just my way of pointing to those arguments.

I think you are correcting what I said last night that might have been slightly misleading, when I was emphasizing, as a theist, that God is personal. I also need to recognize that we do have impersonal philosophical language with which to describe God's relation to the world. And referring to the medieval scholastics is one of the things that we need to do. That's part of theism as well. Theists believe that the universe we live in is ontologically dependent upon God. And that needs to be said philosophically.

Dawkins, to his credit, does take up St. Thomas' five ways of knowing God, or proofs for the existence of God. And then he argues against them trying to show that each one fails to demonstrate the existence of God. Well, I think what you are saying, and I would agree, is that is a fair approach. One ought to carry on those kinds of discussions; and let's see who wins, St. Thomas or Richard Dawkins. I think that is a reasonable thing to do.

When it comes to God as the first cause, Dawkins thinks that he is able to demonstrate that St. Thomas' argument does not work. Then, when Dawkins turns to the question of where did the universe come from, he says, "I don't know. None of us can know." I just find that very interesting. To me that says the conversation is not over yet. I think it is one that can continue.

From my own work in trying to reconcile Darwin's evolutionary model with the Christian understanding of creation, I've gone back again and again to St. Thomas' distinction between primary and secondary cause. I do that because one of the most important features of evolutionary theory is nature's own self-organization. And if that is really the case, and it seems to be pretty observable, there is a way of placing that within the notion of secondary causation that seems to make a lot of sense to me.

That doesn't solve all problems for the theist though; because then how do you defend yourself against deism? God might have started the whole thing and sent evolution rolling down the bowling alley of time, self-organizing itself. The theist of course wants God to be continually involved, and not just at the beginning.

There is a way of understanding primary causation in the tradition of both Augustine and St. Thomas, whereby God's sustaining the world is a moment-by-moment thing. It's not just once in the past. It is contemporary. And I would like to add that what happens as God sustains the world in its very existence is that in each moment God is releasing the world from the grip of the past. That opens us to freedom or contingency and new possibilities in the future, while at the same time maintaining the continuity of physical reality.

I think that this is part of what it means to say that God is primary cause. Let me say that there are still some wrinkles that need to be ironed out. But basically I am finding that the distinction between primary and secondary causation may be one of the best ways of keeping the conversation between science's understanding of nature in terms of self-organization and Christian theology in tandem.

e) Contingency and Chance

Question: Think about one of Dawkins' intellectual ancestors, Jacques Monod. For Monod chance and necessity are the ingredients of the universe. And here you are attributing a divine undergirding for both of those.

Peters: Right, and Monod thought that chance supports atheism. To me that describes God's action in the world.

Question [continued]: A combination of those two [chance and necessity] is essential for explaining what he saw as the evolution of life. And one might say more generally too, that unless you have real contingency in the cosmos, all you can do is claim that a chance event is something with a cause external to the boundaries of your system. And chance is then just some factor that you had not accounted for. You know that it is a closed system and there's no real contingency. So here, perhaps, questions like, "well, what did you expect the cosmos to be like?" and "What difference would it make?" are pushing us toward a better answer to the question than just saying, "God is a personal reality and physics deals with impersonal realities."

Peters: You know, maybe we are getting somewhere.

f) God Hypothesis

Question: I want to pick up on this God Hypothesis. I think at a minimum it ought to be put up as a theory just like evolutionary theory is. It is certainly more than a hypothesis. A lot of people at least believe that it is up there at a theory level, and we are just working on the small details within it.

Peters: Right. We're defining theory here as a hypothesis with a lot of credible support.

Question [continued]: Just like the evolutionary theory, it is *Theory* with a capital T. It strikes me that if you approach it that way, then at least Richard Dawkins has a bigger problem, because he is not addressing a single item. It also seems to me that he is using science sort of like as a deaf scientist saying, "I won't believe in music until I can see it for myself." Is it possible that we simply will not be able to use science in order to prove or disprove God's existence? And how do we develop that concept to address some of the evangelical atheists?

Peters: You don't think that your appreciation of music is merely a biological adaptation in your evolutionary background, do you? You don't need to answer that. I'm trying to get the point of your argument. Is that these higher faculties we have—music, aesthetics—are specially tuned to God, who is transcendent, the issue?

I think, whether we like it or not, we have to go back to the pointer idea. Yes, these things point to a God who transcends us. And in the history of the human race we've been thankful, not just Christians, but people in other cultures as well, to the gods for giving us the gifts of poetry and music. In ancient Greece it was the gods who sort of whispered poetry into the ears of the poets. And I found a line in the Qur'an which I thought was interesting: God is responsible for the metaphors. Okay, there goes the literal reading of the Qur'an, if God is responsible for the metaphors, right?

Or we could come up with an alternative explanation, and Dawkins would certainly like to provide one. He may say, "Oh, but this is just an adaptation, through the long evolutionary development, to our environment. Our musical sensibilities are the fittest surviving. There is really no transcendent basis for these kinds of things." I don't know how to adjudicate that kind of thing. But that might have been your point by saying that this is a theory or hypothesis.

Although you did not ask this, I'm going to make this comment. There is a way in which one can think of certain aspects of Christian theology as hypothetical as well. We don't really have the opportunity to compare our belief in God with the objective God to see whether or not we get confirmation. We can't do that. It's not a possibility. So in some ways, intellectually, our belief in God is hypothetical in character. It is subject to confirmation or disconfirmation. St. Paul in first Corinthians 13 says, "Now we see through a glass darkly, but then (eschatologically) face to face." So the things that we know about God have a necessarily hypothetical character to them.

Now maybe they have the status of a theory, which is to say that they are well supported. But there is still that element of yet-to-be-confirmed component to it. And I think it is possible for the person of the deepest faith to still learn something new about God tomorrow. And it's also a link, I think, with science at its healthiest. I don't think, given that this is the way science and theology are, that you can persuade Dawkins rationally that he is making a mistake. You can suggest that, but I don't think you can persuade him.

g) Atheist Lapses

Question: I have been interested in the lapses which various people involved in the evangelical atheist movement seem to make every once in awhile. For example Carl Sagan had a couple of confessional moments about the mystical side of human nature during an interview. And in *Consilience* Edward O. Wilson attributes his scientific creativity to the religious impulses which were part of his initial formation and his Baptist upbringing. And in Stephen Jay Gould's *Rocks of Ages* there are some passages that almost seem to not belong.

Peters: The lapses of the atheists....When I was a kid I saw a TV show with a skit by Carl Reiner.[1] He was standing behind a podium with "AA" on it. Of course you are thinking Alcoholics Anonymous but he announces that it is "Atheists Anonymous." And oh, yes, for years he had the habit of being religious. And he explained all the things that were wrong with being religious, and how hard he worked to become an atheist. And he said he finally achieved full atheism. He even put it to the test. He was walking home from work one day and he passed by the church he used to attend. And there were two of his former Christian friends loitering in the doorway who said, "Come on in for a quickie prayer." But he said, "No." And marched on. And then he said, "I am a fully committed atheist and I thank God for it." So, there are lapses that you are pointing out here.

And Sagan, Gould, and Wilson do sort of lapse into religious sensibilities. I think with Sagan, and I never knew the man, there must have been some sublimation going on there. When you get to the book and movie, *Contact*, I mean, that is about as religious as you can get. And Sagan almost says that his scientific understanding of the universe fills all that a religious person would need. When you see *Contact*, you get everything including Resurrection. So the religious sensibilities are very much at work. It's just that you've got them secularized. So they don't go away.

I am not remembering the passage in Wilson that you are talking about.

Stephen Jay Gould had a wonderful sense of humor, so I wasn't always exactly sure which remark was the most serious. He wrote *Rocks of Ages* where he formulates his NOMA[2] view that science and religion can exist side-by-side and each have their separate domain, or separate magisterium, and need not conflict, in direct response to Pope John Paul II's statement on evolution in October of 1996. Gould was sort of celebrating the Catholic Church's coming into an arena of the relationship between science and faith that he could live with and accept. And it appeared as though he was showing a lot of respect for religion.

Well, the next year was the year in which he was leaving the presidency of the American Association for the Advancement of Science, and some of you were there. I was there for his speech on science and religion. He said the war between science and religion is now over. And, he said, "we have won!"

By "we" he meant the scientists. Religion has no credibility left. It is utterly decimated. And now we can be nice to religious people because they really don't have any weapons left in their arsenal. And so there was that kind of other side, the jingoistic side.

And then he said that even though he himself holds this position strongly, he has an Episcopal wife and he loves to sing in the church choir, especially the Hallelujah Chorus during Advent. Imagine that!

2. Ethics

a) Cultural leaps

Question: At a certain point in the complexity of things there appear leaps. People like Stephen Jay Gould, try to account for these in an agnostic sense. He wants to keep the scientific discipline separate. I think there are ways, even when using the language of mutation, or chance, to account for those leaps. Could you comment on this?

Peters: Would those be biological mutations or cultural mutations?

Question [continued]: Both.

Peters: I don't believe in cultural mutations. Biological mutations, yes. That's empirical. Cultural mutations, I'm not sure.

Question [continued]: I think there can be pretty major cultural leaps. A speech like in Washington, DC, by Martin Luther King can shift the whole consciousness of the people. That's a fairly significant speech.

Peters: Let me just say that I agree with the phenomenon.

b) Human Ethical Response

Question: In each of your lectures you have not only discussed theological elements, but you have discussed certain ethical responsibilities that we have. To the overarching question," Where in the world is God?" you have given us the answers that God is beyond, God is intimate, and God promises. I wonder if you could also give us a succinct formulation of the ethical side. The human-ethical response is also part of the answer.

Peters: If I were to do that, I would probably add a fourth, following after promises. I think that the basic ethical response for a Christian, and maybe implicitly for non-Christians as well, is to take positive action in such a way as to make the world a better place.

And I think what you get in the vision of say, Isaiah with the Peaceable Kingdom, or the vision that you get in the book of Revelation with the New Jerusalem, is what a better place looks like. So, your and my ethical responsibility is to live our lives in such a way that we influence the world around us in light of that vision. That's kind of the long and the short of Ted Peters' understanding of ethics.

Note that this is different than some conservative moralities that think "God has given us a set of laws and if we obey these laws then we are good." There are many people who want to think of ethics in that fashion, but I am not working with that model. I am working with the model that claims we have both a responsibility and an opportunity to make the world a better place. And that's what the vision of God's future is drawing us towards.

Usually when I try to deal with ethical issues I like to do it that way. I am sympathetic with that side of Robert Oppenheimer.[3] During the break one of you said, "Oh, he was so naïve." Still, I am sympathc with his, saying, "Oh, my gosh! We have let a wild dragon loose on the world now with atomic energy. Is there anyway we can get the dragon sort of back into chains again. Oh yes, maybe an international atomic energy commission in which the nations would give up some of their sovereignty might be the way."

I just want to say, I wish he had succeeded. Because he did have a vision for how we could protect the planet from at least one of the evils. He failed, and we no longer have that protection. At any rate, I think the route of ethics I would like to follow would be something like that.

c) Spirituality and Race Relations

Question: I think there has been real progress on the spiritual side. We can see it just looking back a century. We no longer have the themes of ethnic group superiority, racial superiority, and Nazi eugenics has come and gone.

There has really been visible and measurable progress made. It's in the short term, on the order of decades or less, that we don't see anything.

When you look over centuries, particularly over millennia, I think you can say that the world as we see it today, with a large component of Christianity, is a whole lot better than what was going on under the Romans and the Greeks 2000 years ago. And that, I think, really is measurable, and it shows that there is spiritual growth by the entire body of mankind together.

Peters: I would like to both say yes to that, and qualify it. When I visit the Roman Coliseum, and remember what happened there—athletes died while the crowd cheered— there is no question that athletic contests today are not like that. I like our athletic contests because of this change....well, except hockey. So let me just accept what you said, but then turn nasty.

How do you account for the genocide in Rwanda in the mid 1990s? Two ethnic groups, the Hutus and the Tutsis, had really lived in peace for quite a while. And then suddenly, bang, nearly 900,000 people were murdered in a 90 day period. How did that happen?

I do a lot of work in genetics. I have a number of graduate students helping me. One of them is specializing in the eugenics movement, trying to reassess the history of the eugenics movement. And he goes to web sites and watches what's happening on the web sites. He says there are racist groups who are just hovering over the Hap Map that the National Institutes of Health is doing, which is going to try to trace the genetic history of the human race. What they want to do is to find the genetic basis for racism. And when they get it, then they are going to say, see, science shows us this.

If we think of history, cultural history, as contingent—and you are right we have made this enormous progress in terms of understanding racial equality, etc.—what happens if suddenly history changes, and one of these groups come to power?

That is basically what happened in the 1920s in Germany. I mean, Germany could have gone the other way. They had a liberal society. But they didn't. They went the Nazi route.

Well what happens if the White Arian Nation somehow or other gets hold of this science and gets hold of some political clout?

I think Western civilization should be proud of its social achievements, there is no question about it. But I don't think there is a built-in guarantee that it is going to get still better.

At the end of Klaatu's speech, he says, "The decision is yours." And I hate to sound like a moralistic preacher. But you know what? That is where we are. It really is a decision for the present generation whether the next generation is going to be better on issues of racial parity, economic justice, and peace. It's going to be a decision that has to be made by every generation. So there is no built-in principle of moral advance.

3. Extraterrestrials

a) Character of UFO Communities

Question: Do you think that the UFO myth could have originated with the masses who are not scientific? This could have been a response to scientific innovation. People may be acknowledging the dual nature of science as both a triumph while knowing sin. Could the UFO myth be a coping mechanism, so people can deal with the idea of technology?

Peters: Excellent question, and my answer is going to be a little bit nuanced. I think that I am going to say, yes, that it is a coping mechanism but, No, it doesn't represent an inability to deal with science. Quite the opposite. It is promulgated primarily by people who love science and who are scientifically trained, in many cases.

Over the years I've tried to spend time with UFO communities. One of the things that amazes me is that they love scientific thinking, especially in Western Europe, North America, Australia, Japan, and Russia, where the UFO phenomenon is big. They love scientific thinking! Many of them are highly trained. They tend to be engineers.

For a long time they had a research project on the propulsion of flying saucers from one planet to another. This is a scientific problem; and we're going to solve it.

The whole framework for thinking about the UFO myth, at least in the countries that I have mentioned, is science. So what I think is important is that Western culture in general loves science. It is everywhere, and the UFO myth is treated by the UFO believers as a scientific question.

But you've got to back up a little bit. You have to go back to the middle of the 19th century, and especially the last of the 19th century. There you've got a merging of science and religion. Science was the new kid on the block. Everybody was falling in love with science. And the traditional religions didn't have any room for it. So the new religious movements got names having something to do with science.

Look at all of the religious movements in the last half of the 19th century. Most of them have science in their title. *Christian Science* has survived, but a lot of them that didn't survive thought of themselves as being scientific.

So I just want to say that science is a part of the myth. Those in establishment science, who don't like UFO's, want to patent science for themselves. "We are the scientists. Everybody else is emotionally weak, and they need to cope, because they can't really handle hard-nosed science." Well, it's a self congratulatory image that establishment people tell themselves when they want to marginalize others.

But if you actually go into UFO groups and spend time with them, you find that they're running around with Ph.D.'s in engineering and they are really trying to treat the UFO phenomenon scientifically. Why? Because science is the only language that our Western culture can use.

So what I want to say about the myth part is that within the framework of scientific language, these religious meanings and sensibilities arise. In the final scene of the movie—*The Day the Earth Stood Still*—we are looking at what? The stars. And the flying saucer is a light that becomes a star as the movie closes.

Well, as far back in time as we can go, the stars have been symbols of the divine. And so the merging of the UFO's with the stars is, at a symbolic level, the divine coming to visit us, but as a technological product. So I think that the important thing the UFO myth does is to show the ubiquitous role of scientific thinking. Things that are overtly religious have to get sublimated within it. If you look only at the skeptic's interpretation of UFOs, you won't see it.

And I want to add, that science fiction does not understand the UFO phenomenon either. These movies about flying saucers follow a prescribed script: planet earth is at war with ETI, and we are going to have this battle, and we are going to create this machine that will ward off the invading enemy; this is science fiction. Such movies do not understand at a cultural level how science comes to save us. Only *The Day the Earth Stood Still* (1951) and *Close Encounters of the Third Kind* (1977) are authentic to the UFO phenomenon. Here you get this interesting marriage of science and religion at the level of symbol.

I know that was a long answer. But I think it is important. That is why I kind of like visiting these people firsthand and asking, "What do you think?" Their science might not be very good, but in their mind it is still science.

b) Multiple Incarnations

Question: I want to consider multiple incarnations. The story of the incarnation of Jesus on earth is very important for us. And the incarnation elsewhere would be important for another people as well. So I want to consider that there were, or will be multiple incarnations. Do you have any response to that?

Peters: As I said, I'm still thinking about this. But I think there are at least three different ways of thinking about the incarnation.

Paul Tillich, who holds to multiple incarnations, would argue that in each civilization or in each species, God would need to come in the form of that species so that they would know him. So what's going on there? Well, it's an understanding of incarnation as revelation. The point is that what we need to do is to come to know God, and God will help us out by entering the realm in which we can understand. That's one way to think about it.

Another way is to think of the saving work of Jesus Christ as efficacious. Somehow or other what Jesus did, through his death and resurrection, was to change the way the cosmos works, so that now our relationship to God is based upon forgiveness and grace. If that is the case, then the incarnation would affect everything in the universe. And we would only need one saving event.

A third way to think about it would be to consider that, in the history of this event, God is the savior. The transcendent God is the savior. And this is the occasion in which that event takes place.

This third one is the most puzzling. The first two are pretty obvious. If it's revelatory in character, then we need multiple incarnations. If it's an efficacious work of atonement, then we only need one incarnation. But if God as Father is responsible for the saving work, maybe God is always doing this. And if there is another world somewhere and another species of intelligent being, then God is probably already at work there too. But maybe not in the same way as has happened here. Anyway, I'm just kind of laying out the possibilities here, and not really knowing for certain which is the most adequate one.

c) Faith and Redemptive Violence

Question: I'd like to comment on two aspects of this ETI myth that you talked about. The one, which was expressed in various ways, most dramatically perhaps by Paul Davies,[4] that discovering extraterrestrial life would lead to the collapse of faith. That strikes me as strongly reminiscent of this notion about which we have heard a lot in the last couple years. It is kind of perennial around the *da Vinci Code*, the discovery of the gospel of Judas, etc. I think it is related to the belief in a conspiracy myth in which the Vatican has access to secret knowledge, and so forth, which would be devastating if it came out. This strikes me as all of a piece, that it is really based mostly on a misunderstanding of what faith is and how it shapes society. And so it shouldn't concern us overly much. It is part of a whole cultural phenomenon.

The second issue is the ability of science to save us. That strikes me as at least parallel to what has been called the myth of redemptive violence, that there are things that we can take in hand. And of course these are frequently dovetailed with technology. I wonder whether these manifestations of science, or of the kind of defensive technology like the Star Wars missile shield, represent nonviolent versions of the myth of redemptive violence. These allow us to protect ourselves without bearing the burden of possible guilt associated with even justification.

Peters: Let me just ask why you would claim that something like Star Wars defensive system represents this? Would that not be the myth of redemptive violence full form?

Question [continued]: Because it fends off these myths. We don't have to kill people necessarily. It just defends.

Peters: It's because it is a defensive technology rather than an offensive technology?

Question [continued]: Yes, it saves us the burden of potential guilt of even just war. So in this respect I think it does perpetuate the kind of mythology that salvation is somewhere other than in trust in God.

Peters: As I understand the myth of redemptive violence, this is not peculiar to our modern technological society. It's been around for as long as the human race has. And in some ways the events of Jesus' death are over against the myth of redemptive violence, which was operative at the time.

So you and I just never get away from it. Ronald Reagan's Star Wars[5] was just one more manifestation of this, or President Bush's saying, if we don't stop them in Iraq we'll have to do it in our own shores. There is the myth of redemptive violence at work. We are not going to get away from that, I don't think. It's like the water the goldfish swims in; it's everywhere.

And on the *da Vinci Code*, my students keep asking me about the bones of Jesus and the ostuaries. And I keep trying to get to the discovery channel to see this show. I haven't seen it yet. I notice that *Time* magazine had a little article about the stuff, and I do want to see the show when it is available.

Yesterday I went to the Old Bag Factory[6] here in Goshen, and I found a shop that sold kind of kitschy religious things. And there was an Easter resurrection crèche scene, which I had never before seen in my life. Jesus is coming out of the tomb. This is great, I think, I really want this. So now I've got Jesus, and Mary Magdalene, and two lambs. It was $85. But she said, "Oh, this is on sale, 25% off." I thought, oh, good, this is my lucky day! And as I am walking out I am thinking, is that because they found the bones of Jesus?

d) Evolution and Doctrine of Progress

Question [seminary student]: I'm interested in your idea that the ETI myth includes a doctrine of progress, which claims that if other civilizations have existed longer than us, then they would have evolved more than we have. But it seems also to be equally a doctrine of progress to say that we have evolved the farthest of any civilizations that might exist. Maybe you can comment on that.

Peters: If I understand your question, you agree that the concept of evolution and the doctrine of progress have been inextricably intertwined from the beginning. And the scientific community has been very carefully trying to extricate progress from it. Francisco Ayala would be an example of someone who wants to do a "surgical operation" on evolution to remove the doctrine of progress.

If you look at Darwin's *Origin of Species*,[7] you will note that he kind of waffles. On the one hand he really wants to reject the doctrine of progress, and say these are random events without any direction. But on the other hand he doesn't want to leave people in a bad mood when they are done. So he has these flourishes about how wonderful it is that this long process as produced us, the human race. The idea that you and I are products of a long, progressive development is always there in what Darwin writes.

In Berkeley we have a furniture store called The Evolution Furniture Store. And they think that they have the most progressive furniture. So that is kind of a popular view.

Christian de Duve,[8] the biologist, likes to emphasize that we human beings are only a stage along evolution's way, and that we can look forward into the future to ever higher advances. Now, de Duve is not adding progress to evolution; rather, he assumes evolution and progress already come in a single package. And the hard nosed scientists who eat sauerkraut for breakfast are the ones that want to get the progress out, so that evolution becomes reduced to non-purposive chance.

Question [continued]: Maybe I have not understood exactly what it is you are saying. I think you are critiquing the doctrine of progress that results in the belief that other civilizations have evolved more than we have. So is your alternative to that the claim that there are no civilizations that have evolved farther than we have?

Peters: No, because I want to leave that as an empirical question. When they contact us we'll ask them. Is your science better than ours or not? And I think whatever they answer will be the final answer. So I don't want to pre-judge that now; because if I do that it is kind of an ideology.

My caution has to do with your and my life here on earth, and whether or not we believe that progress in science and technology will save us. And I want to say, that is risking idolatry if we think it will. Because the track record of science and technology is ambiguous.

On the one hand science has done startling things. On the other hand, life is just as contingent and just as risky and just as dangerous, if not more so, as it was before these achievements of science. So what I want to do is pull out just that question: will progress be salvific? And I want to say, no, it won't. And that's the part of the myth that I am critical of. Unless I meet ETI, I can't make a judgment as to whether or not extraterrestrial intelligent beings exist, and if they do exist whether they are better than us in science and technology or not.

4. Religion

a) Resurrection and the New Creation

Question: I'm aware that you studied with Wolfhart Pannenberg, and when you are talking about resurrection I know of no systematic theologian who has articulated historical bodily resurrection as well as Pannenberg has. And I am wondering, are you talking in "Pannenbergian" style when you talk about the resurrection?

Peters: Yes, very much. I am influenced by Pannenberg theology. I was not actually his student, but I've done a lot of writing in areas in which I am quite dependent upon his thought.

The key point that I was making here—namely, there is an inextricable link between the resurrection of Jesus yesterday and the new creation of tomorrow—is something that Pannenberg says with great eloquence. And what he also says, which I find extremely attractive, is that ontology begins with the future. That is to say, God's creative work is really the new creation.

Where we find ourselves now, in the process of the present creation, is on the way toward a new reality. So, the gravity of this particular vision is really with what you and I would call transformation from our present point of view. Pannenberg also gives me the word *prolepsis*, which I like a lot. Perhaps I use it too much. So my students make jokes about it. The Easter resurrection of Jesus is a prolepsis of the new creation. What happened in Jesus' person on Easter is what will happen to the entire creation at the transformation.

So when we look for those signs, or what Bob Russell would call the precursors in the natural world, I think we want to do it with theological eyes and say, "Lets look for those things that anticipate what we think is the vision of the new creation." That would be a proleptic way of interpreting the natural world.

b) Mormon Addition to Genesis

Question [Mormon biophysicist]: As you went through this I realized you didn't ever do the Mormon perspective.

Mormons, as you probably know, have some additional scriptures. The Bible plus these additional scriptures form a lot of our beliefs. The six verses that I'm going to read to you are verses that are basically Genesis 0 (From the "Pearl of Great Price", Book of Moses 1:30-35). This is a chapter of the book of Moses that we believe was lost. It was originally in the scriptures, but somehow had disappeared. This is the introduction to why we have Genesis. It's the dialogue between Moses and God, before God reveals to him Genesis 1. I'll skip around just a little bit, to keep it to the point.

It says, "And it came to pass that Moses called upon God, saying: Tell me, I pray thee, why these things are so, and by what thou madest them?" So he is saying, why is the universe, and how did you make the universe?

"And the Lord God said unto Moses: For mine own purpose have I made these." I'm not going to tell you why I made them.

"Here is wisdom and it remaineth in me." But now he says how he made them. "And by the word of my power, have I created them, which is mine Only Begotten Son, who is full of grace and truth."

And here is the key verse. "And worlds without number have I created; and I also created them for mine own purpose; and by the Son I created them, which is mine Only Begotten. And the first man of all men have I called Adam, which is many. But only an account of this earth, and the inhabitants thereof, give I unto you. For behold, there are many worlds that have passed away by the word of my power. And there are many that now stand, and innumerable are they unto man; but all things are numbered unto me, for they are mine and I know them."

Then he proceeds and a few verses later start out "And in the beginning created God the heaven and the earth," and this is now the creation story of *this* earth, and I'm not going to tell you about the other earths.

Peters: So which book does that appear in?

Question [continued]: this would be in the collective group of books called *The Pearl of Great Price*, in Moses chapter 1.

c) Sanctification and Christian Growth

Question: We talked earlier about how the idea of sanctification, Christian perfection, and growing from one degree of glory to the next. You said some helpful things. I would like to hear them again.

Peters: Let me say some things that I didn't say before. Remember that I am a Lutheran, and Lutherans have not solved all theological problems.

One of the things about the Lutherans is that their doctrine of sanctification is not very good. When it comes to sanctification I kind of look enviously at John Wesley, because he has this doctrine of Christian perfection. Growing in the love of the Lord, he imagines, is a process in which the Holy Spirit, day by day, helps us to love increasingly like God loves.

And we Lutherans don't have that kind of a thing. What Luther says is that every day you get up and you remember your baptism, when you were forgiven, and then you live like an ordinary human being.

So I got my Lutheran faculty together and said, "I really want to talk about this relationship that takes us from justification to sanctification, and just see about the Methodists or others who have this understanding of progress in growth of the spirit." And I was sort of touting John Wesley's doctrine of Christian perfection as a form of sanctification that might be attractive to us. I had this colleague named Bob Smith, who looked at me and said, ""Ted, do you love God?" I said, "Oh, yeah, I do." "Do you think you are better today than you were yesterday?" I said, "Gee, Bob, I don't think I am." "Well, what are you talking about?" And basically it kind of went bust. I mean the Lutherans just have a hard time with sanctification.

And yet I know that other Christian groups really do have a robust understanding of sanctification, in which there is progress in the growth of our godliness. So let me just make that as an observation.

Now, that has to do with individual persons and their relationship to the Holy Spirit. What about society as a whole? Can there be spiritual growth in a culture? Yes, I think that there can be, as we were saying in our conversation.

I remember a colleague who used to teach with me at Loyola who said, "You know, if you just look at the facts, race relations in America are much better now than they were 30 years ago. There's just no question about it by any objective measure. Are we perfect? No, we are not. But we are better." So there is an index of social justice in which you could mark improvement.

Does that mean it is inevitable? Does that mean that 10 years from now we'll be even better, or 20 years from now even better still? Well, no, it's sort of contingent, year to year, as to what is going to happen in our society.

In the 1960s when I was a graduate student, I was very liberal, "lefter than thou." Man, if the next administration in Washington will do just the right thing, we're going to have economic justice, we're going to have racial equality, we're going to have international peace. And, you know, the next administration gets into office and they are just as dumb and just as militaristic as the one that went out! If not worse! And you get this feeling that we never learn.

In the case of the Bush administration, we knew that Al-Qaeda had said that they planned on copying the methods of the Vietcong back in the Vietnam War in the 1960s, when the United States shows up in the Middle East. And you know what? They did! And we fell into the trap. And you want to say, there wasn't even any progress in military intelligence over 30 years. How did that happen?

And I end up considering such things as a Christian understanding of human nature. You know, God created us good, but we are deluded by megalomania and such things. You can almost see it in our leadership, how megalomania causes darkness in the eyes and things like that.

So, these are just anecdotes. And we are not even talking about science and technology. We are asking whether culture can progress. And when we ask even the simple question of whether culture can learn from its past mistakes, we have historians to remind us of what happened. It seems to me we just can't make moral progress we just don't do that. Yes, it's funny. We learn it, but it doesn't make us better. We learn that we don't learn. I think that's the best way of putting it. Now, you speak to the idea. Is there such a thing as progress in these important spiritual and ethical matters?

5. Religion and Science Dialogue

a) Religion as Biologically Based

Question: There are some people in the religious and scientific areas of study who believe that religion is a response to science. What do you think?

Peters: Help me to understand who believes that religion is a response to science.

Question [continued]: Ursula Goodenough, for one.

Peters: I do not understand Ursula's position on that. I mean, there is this kind of a sociobiological attempt to explain religion as an adaptation. But is that what we are talking about?

Question [continued]: As I understand her she is saying that she doesn't believe that religion is a spontaneous phenomenon in the world.

Peters: It might be rooted in our physiology or our physiological development?

Question [continued]: She thinks that it is rooted within nature.

Peters: So the question is, if we could retrace our relationship with nature, quite specifically our evolutionary history, would we find the development of human religion to be an extension of our biological development, or the appearance of intelligence?

I want to consider that these kinds of theories probably have a seed of truth to them, at least in the sense that once human intelligence crosses a certain evolutionary threshold and we begin to imagine things that are counterfactual. For example, if you have to decide whether you're going to take the road to the right or the road to the left, you have to imagine whether there are wild beasts on one road and bad weather on the other. You have to make these decisions, so that you have to imagine things that are not immediately perceptual in character. One could then reconstruct a possible history of the rise of religious sensibilities and human consciousness. I don't find it unreasonable to do that. So if Ursula's point is that religion is not the result of a visitation from a divine figure, but is really the result of the growth of the human mind, I would say, well, yes, maybe it did happen that way. I'm not sure.

That would be a part of a whole family of important questions such as, if we share a common ancestry with other primates—apes, chimpanzees, gorillas, bonobos, and orangutans—at what point did we in our history cross a threshold at which all kinds of new cultural things happen? Religion would be just one of these. When it comes to a Christian, Muslim, or Jew, I think that these three traditions depend upon *special revelation*, and it wouldn't matter whether a biologically based religion preceded them or not. God calls Abraham, and God visits Moses, and either that is true or false. The fact that Abraham had a general kind of Middle Eastern religious disposition before God called him is utterly irrelevant to what happened later.

So I guess I would say, as a theologian, Ursula offers an interesting theory. But I don't think it would make any *theological* difference whatsoever as to whether or not our religious sensibilities are the product of biological development.

b) Pluralism, Origins, and Ideas

Question: The pluralists believe that every religion is equal. Each religion is a different path up the same mountain. There is no attempt to undermine any believed reality or any religion. Would you then say that the pluralistic perspective is the best possible approach to religious unity?

Peters: Let me just say that among my friends who are pluralists—and most of my friends are pluralists—what they really want is peace between the religious traditions. They don't need religious unity. What they need is to somehow or other stop the competition. They would like to see all religions, but Christianity in particular, stop aligning themselves with imperialistic economic and political forces. They think that if Christians in the advantaged world would attribute parity or equality to other religious traditions in the disadvantaged world, then economic and social imperialism would lose its religious base.

The origin of this, actually goes back to John Hick, whom I cited here, and who I think is one of the best philosophers of religion of our time. He described how he came to this position. He was in London. Many Muslims had come into England as guest workers. Their children were in the public schools, where they all had to take a required course in Christianity. And they said, "But we are not Christians. Could you come up with a course in Islam for us?" Legally they couldn't. Well, Hicks said, "This isn't fair." Public school's teaching Christianity, etc, isn't fair. So that's what sent him down this path. He thought the public schools ought to give courses on Islam for the Islamic children, and Christian courses for the Christian children, and stuff like that. Hick's concept of "the Real" that transcends every tradition-specific symbol for the divine is offered as an attempt to provide a grounding for treating the other religions as real equals.

My criticism is not the pluralist's motivation. I think it is a healthy motivation. The problem is this: it's not going to work. You're not going to convince a suicide bomber or even the most moderate Muslim by saying, "Look, your religion is only a perspective." I don't think you're going to convince the average Christian of this either, let alone, members of other religious traditions. The pluralist approach asks each religious tradition to sacrifice its deep insights to a more superficial unity. So I think that practically it is not going to work.

Nevertheless, the ethic of treating people in other religious traditions with respect is a good thing. The whole world needs that. We really do. And I just think we need another basis for it than this doctrinal pluralism. I'm just repeating myself, but I wanted to be sure that I understood your question.

c) Talking Without Quarreling

Question: If you take the three themes that you used as challenges to Christianity—evangelical atheism, pluralism, and Islam—it seems that they could also be used as emblematic of the typology that is often used to describe the debate between science and religion. We see this, for example, in the subtitle of Ian Barbour's little book a couple years ago, *When Science Meets Religion: Enemies, Strangers, or Partners?* (May 16, 2000). You might say that even though you pointed out that the evangelical atheist position is not synonymous with science, nevertheless they seem prefer science without religion.

On the other hand, we may take the Islamic point of view, as you were trying to present it last night. Even though there is obviously a tremendous scientific tradition within the history of Islam, what you presented as the challenge was that, in terms of cosmic meaning, they prefer religion without science.

Then in the pluralistic position not only are all the religions of varying perspectives, but science itself might be viewed as just one of many perspectives. So, in terms of an irenic coexistence, this point of view may consider a partnership between science and religion. Or if the language of incommensurability enters, then maybe there's an estrangement or alienation. I ask you to comment on that.

Your mention of C. S. Lewis reminded me of a comment that G. K. Chesterton made in describing C. S. Lewis' lifelong relationship with his brother Cecil. He said that throughout their lives they argued endlessly. But they never quarreled about anything. And that would be a nice way to think about the proper relationship between science and religion.

Peters: You mean that the proper relationship between science and religion would be one of talking endlessly without quarreling? I think I like that. Science at its best is an open and progressive growth in knowledge, in which our perspective is constantly changing as we gain knowledge about the world. And in many ways science is good sport; it's fun. In contrast, we quite frequently think religion is dogmatic, rigid, fixed, and unchanging. For this reason, religion ain't no fun. Yet, in Berkeley at the Center for Theology and Natural Sciences, at the Zygon Center in Chicago, and many other of the focal groups in which scientists and theologians come together, usually the theologians are like scientists in the sense that they are really looking forward to learning new things, expanding their horizons, and adapting. I think that for good, successful relationships of the type that you are talking about, where there is talking without quarreling, people representing both science and religion, there should be a willingness to have free play, enjoy the conversation, and hope that it will lead to new things.

d) Murphy and Lakatos

Question: There are some tensions that we face. There is a need to be flexible and yet hold onto an orthodox core. I appreciate what Nancey Murphy said about using the philosophy of Imre Lakatos in research programs. We don't want to hinder our research program. But our research program has a protective belt around it that is socially embodied and historically extended. Can you comment on how we can hold to core concepts like the doctrine of the Trinity and the incarnation and yet be fluid in our understanding of how those change in time?

Peters: I think you have given the answer, not the question. Nancey Murphy's use of Imre Lakatos I find to be very illuminating and it's one of the ways in which she can demonstrate what is in common between a progressive research program in science, and a theology that is not defensive, a theology which is open to a change.

Yes, there are going to be theological commitments at the core that define the basic horizon from which the theologian works. In the case of Christians and Muslims as well as theologically oriented Jews, faith is really based on special revelation. And that's a pretty solid core there. To what extent the traditions, customs, and cultural forms that our churches have developed over two millennia are malleable and changeable, we will have to wait and see.

I drive a little bit of a wedge between the theologian and the tradition of the church here. I think the theologian has the right to go back to the basic sources and rethink. In some way Nancey Murphy's use of Lakatos will show, I predict, that when the theologian does that, that the orthodox core is going to hold, even though that outer belt might fluctuate a little bit. I think that's the way it works, and I don't think anybody gets hurt with that particular image.

What Richard Dawkins would like, of course, would be to eliminate the foundation for the orthodox core of a religious vision. Well, those of us who represent the Christian faith can react negatively, saying, "Oh, this is awful" and use *ad hominem* arguments, which are kind of fun, but not necessarily helpful. Or we could use it as an opportunity to go back and re-examine the core and say, "Well, at least for me, I think the core is worth keeping, even though I think I can listen to these critical sorts of things with regard to some of the corollaries that we have developed over the centuries."

e) Spectrum of thought

Question: In your book *Can You Believe in God and Evolution*[9] you have some very nice charts characterizing such positions as interventionist and non-interventionist. But you did not identify your position. Would you place yourself somewhere between Warfield and Tielhard? And could you talk about the idea of divine governance in the world?

Peters: What she is mentioning is in this book called *Can You Believe in God and Evolution?*, which I co-authored with Marty Hewlett, who is the virologist that I had mentioned earlier. We try to put the various positions in the evolution controversy on a spectrum. The spectrum has to do with God's action in the natural world.

At one extreme where we have materialism or atheism, where there is no God. So there is no action of God in the world.

At the other extreme we put God's intervention in the world. There we locate first the scientific creationists, for whom God takes action and all of nature responds. Right next to them we put the Intelligent Design people, for whom God also acts in nature and then nature responds to God's action. Then in the middle between those two positions we line up that group of people that we call theistic evolutionists. The most conservative of these is B. B. Warfield,[10] the person and theologian who gave us the doctrine of biblical inerrancy that led to American fundamentalism. At the other extreme is Teilhard de Chardin, who has this total integration of the evolutionary worldview with Christian theology. And then in the middle we place my friends and most of the people who come here to Goshen to lecture.

Okay, so where do I belong? Well, it's with those people in the middle there that I am likely to have a Saturday night barbecue. The creationists are not going to invite me over. And the atheists are not going to invite me over. But the theistic evolutionists probably will. So it's a loose kind of fellowship with them.

Part of the answer to your question is a research agenda with my colleague Bob Russell and some of the others with whom you have worked here: Antje Jackelén,[11] and Philip Hefner.[12] What we are looking for is the non-miraculous action of God in the natural world.

Does that mean we don't know believe in miracles? No, it means miracles are not the research agenda. The research agenda has to do with the non-interventionist action of God within the natural world, especially the long story of evolutionary development. So I would put myself right smack in the middle of that group. That doesn't mean that I am disavowing miracles. It means that miracles are just not on the agenda. Now, does that help?

Question [continued]: Yes. Then I was just wondering if you would talk a little bit more about governance.

Peters: Let me just say that that is a real tough nut to crack. It is an important item, though. And certainly all Christian theists believe in divine governance of the world. But I am just having a hard time giving you a rational description of God's noninterventionist action.

6. Science

a) Reductionism and God Talk

Question: With training in mathematics and physics, I am a bit of a reductionist at heart. What would you say to scientists who are ontological reductionists in thinking that primarily all is physics or can be known by science, and don't consider the universe as open to a God who is immanent or gracious?

Peters: I wonder if that is two questions or one. One would be the question of reductionism. And then there is the question of whether or not reductionism is related to the possibility of a gracious God. Actually, you know, I kind of baited some of the scientists last night by asking, "Can you find God in the equations, and if so how?" I'm going to work with Dawkins' assumption that you look at the equations and you don't see God.

I might be wrong in this. But I tend to think of those things that we designate as religious, and those things that we consider personal, as existing at higher levels of organization. Reductionism does give us knowledge, to be sure, but it doesn't explain the higher levels of organization, such as the human person, the human mind, and the things that you and I actually think about.

So I don't really ask the physicist to find God in the equations. I know it's sort of disputable, but let me just say that I don't ask the physicist to do that. But I ask human consciousness, at the level we live in every day, to think about that particular topic. Methodological reductionism I find absolutely necessary to pursue science.

That you should have an ontology that is based on that is what I would dispute. I think that your and my intellectual interchange right here at the level of ideas is just as real as the quantum physical activity that is everywhere. And I think that is where God-talk belongs.

b) Contingency and Release

Question: You said that God is the continuing moment-by-moment sustaining power or sustaining cause of the cosmos and that God releases us from the past and allows novelty. Were you speaking there of personal novelty, release from our sins, chance for renewal of life, or also of novelty in all the cosmos?

Peters: Novelty in the entire cosmos, which is what you and I experience as contingency. Not just what we experience, but what we observe as contingent and unpredictable events in the natural world are due to God's releasing the world every moment from the grip of a closed causal nexus.

When we think scientifically about the world, we try to construct a system of laws. You end up moving towards a closed causal nexus. Then how do you explain the fact that events are unpredictable? It would seem to me that on the one hand God's faithfulness explains why there is continuity in the laws and in the material world. On the other hand the fact that each moment has a certain newness to it granted by God means that we are released from the iron grip of past causes. That's what makes the physical world contingent and also makes what you and I experience as human freedom possible.

c) DNA as the Language of God

Question: I'd like to hear your further comment about Francis Collins and his seemingly finding God in the equations, or at least that what we find in science is the language of God. Would you say a little bit more?

Peters: Well, first of all, Francis thinks that DNA is a language. I asked him one time, "You think that DNA is a language, right?"

"Right."

"Do you mean that literally or metaphorically, that it's *like* a language."

"No, no! I mean that literally."

I just have to say, "I don't understand that."

But he is utterly serious about that, and…where's Dr. H.? Maybe after I'm done, you can speak to this question. I'd like to know what your opinion is as to whether DNA is actually a language or not.

I would be so much more cautious than Francis is, when he says literally, "It's a language." The title of his book from last July is *The Language of God.* That takes a second commitment to somehow or other see the language of DNA as actually something that God created specifically. I don't think he goes quite that far. I think that it's more the experience that we all have with DNA. It is so marvelous and so complex that aesthetically we need to appreciate it.

But that's not the same thing as to say that God created it in any kind of literal sense. I'm not sure Francis is all that clear on that or else maybe it's my failure to understand for sure just what he is saying. But what were you thinking when you posed that question?

Question [continued]: Well, I couldn't quite see persons like yourself being quite where he seemed to be. But it raises all kinds of questions, not only is it English, Spanish, Chinese…I would be interested in hearing scientists comment more about that.

Peters: Dr. H. spends a lot of research time with DNA. Do you think DNA is a language?

Dr. H.: I'm certainly no expert to comment. But I do believe that, having read Francis' book, I see aspects of what he is referring to regarding DNA as being a language. So, I embrace that at a high level. But in terms of really getting into the details to be able to put forth exactly why he is saying that, I'd prefer not to go there.

d) DNA as Instruction Manual

Question [physiologist]: I'm a physiologist, and can say a little about this, although I don't consider myself an expert. I don't deal so much with DNA as with the end products of DNA, the proteins that DNA makes. So, I'm one step removed.

I see DNA, not as a language, but as an instruction manual. The trouble is that there's a lot of DNA that isn't instruction. The part that we understand is the instruction part.

There are parts of DNA that are genes that code for specific proteins that make our body. Then there are parts that were originally thought to be simply left over waste pieces. Now more and more of these are found to be saying when this is to be made, and under what conditions it is made, and when do you turn it on and when do you turn off.

So it is still part of the instruction manual, but the instruction manual is saying, "Wait until Saturday 12:00 a.m. to make this particular one, and wait until this particular signal comes in." So it's a very detailed instruction manual. Is DNA a language? I don't think so, but it's a subset of the language, I would think.

e) Physics of Immortality

Question [student]: I was wondering if you could comment on a book I just received. The author is Frank J. Tipler. The book is *The Physics of Immortality*. He makes a bold statement on the back of the book, saying that he has found God in the equations. I was wondering if you had any knowledge of that book, or the man who wrote it, and what you could say about that.

Peters: I do. Frank is a most interesting person. He is a mathematical physicist at Tulane University, and in the 1980s he and John Barrow[13] gave us one of the more sophisticated accounts of the Anthropic Principle in the universe. And so he has been highly respected in that regard.

He considers himself an atheist, raised as a Southern Baptist, and then converted to atheism as a college student intellectual. In the book, *The Physics of Immortality*, published in 1995, interestingly enough, he is going to show, as a physicist, how the concept of the resurrection could be conceived. He doesn't actually give testimony to the existence of God. Quite the opposite. He's going to give an account for resurrection without God. And so he develops this theory based upon what you see in artificial intelligence, namely that human intelligence is a form of computation. We could take human thought processes out of the brain, and put our minds into a computer. And you would carry the consciousness of the human being with it into the computer. So then he projects into the future. As the earth burns up and gets destroyed he claims that we will have developed the technology to transfer human consciousness into non-physical embodiment.

What I think is fiery and delightful about this is that he now, as a physicist, is doing theology, but without God and without special revelation. He actually says, "In the future, theological studies will be within physics departments." I classify this under what I call *scientific imperialism*. The scientific imperialists are different from a Dawkins, who is an advocate of scientism, which is science without religion. Scientific imperialists want science with religion, but they want religion subordinated to the science. Frank Tipler and E. O. Wilson represent two paradigms in which science explains religion better than theologians do. So if Frank Tipler gets his way, I as a theologian won't earn an honest living anymore. Or else I'll have to get a job in the physics department at Tulane.

I got an e-mail from Frank about a month ago. He's got a new book coming out in May. And he'd like to come to Berkeley to talk about it. So I'm kind of anxious to see what's going to be in this book. In the meantime, I have heard rumor that he has returned to Christianity. So we'll see what the new book has to say.

f) Equations as Pointers

Question [physicist]: This has to do with finding God in the equations. I think that different people find pointers toward God in different ways. Physicists and those with considerable mathematical training find a real good pointer to God in the equations. Maxwell's equations and the equations of general relativity are examples. One leading physicist [Eugene Wigner] referred to "the unreasonable effectiveness of mathematics," which is really stunning. You look at this and you say, "Hey, who thought this up!"

Do you find God in the equations? Not exactly. But you sure do find a real good pointer in that direction. And I think that is a very important distinction to keep in mind.

Peters: I like your word *pointer* a lot. I think that might be the best word for what it is we are talking about. And I think we can distinguish between our human experience of love on the one hand, and our experience of the universe, whether seen through the eyes of science or not, on the other. Last evening I quoted Psalm 19 and John Calvin. Both the Psalmist and Calvin are stunned by the magnificence of the stars in the sky. And for them that is a pointer to God. Both of those are premodern. Now we've got science, and we can take a look at the stars in the sky through mathematics.

I want to tell you a story. We have a lot of dialogues at Berkeley between scientists and theologians. One physicist, who was a Hindu (I actually don't remember his name), and I had this boat ride. I sat down and started kind of quizzing him on things. And as he was using the word "God" a lot, it sounded to me like he was talking about God in very personal terms. I know a little bit about Hinduism. So I asked, "Well, tell me in your own thinking, do you think of Brahman in more personal terms or impersonal terms?"

"Oh," he said, "I think of God as being personal."

I asked, "Well, why?"

"Oh," he said, "I'm a scientist. When I think about the 150 billion galaxies, when I think about the speed with which the universe is expanding and the galaxies are separating from each other, when I think about the complexity of star formation, and when I think that the rational structure of everything that is happening in those most distant galaxies is copied right here in my mind so that I can appreciate them, I just want to say, 'thank you' to somebody."

So I like the word "pointer." God might not be in the equations, but we can say "Ah, these equations are telling us something magnificent and wonderful." Dawkins probably would not be impressed by that conversation; but there is a way in which the pointer is there for us to see in which direction it goes.

g) Anthropic Principle

Question: There are books by scientists claiming to have proof of God or evidence of God through science. Often these are based on probabilities. And they try to weave these probabilities together, eventually forming some sort of proof of God. What is your opinion of such efforts to prove or provide evidence for God through just probability? And secondly do you think that scientific atheists like Dawkins completely disregard this methodology, this idea of providing evidence for God through probability?

Peters: Perhaps the best example of what you are talking about might be the Anthropic Principle. Those, who are in favor of the Anthropic Principle, come from physics. They don't come from theology. They take a look at the initial conditions there at the Big Bang, and note that if there had been the slightest fractional difference in such things as the amount of mass in the universe, the speed of expansion and all of these kinds of things, that star formation and planet formation, and all of those things necessary for the Goldilocks planet on which we live would not have resulted.

You could take a minimalist position and say, "The initial conditions made it possible for life to evolve." This would give you a Weak Anthropic Principle. Or you could have a Strong Anthropic Principle and say, "It was inevitable that this would happen." And then you can go back and say, "Why this universe and not another." One answer could be that God designed it that way.

Some people don't like this. Richard Dawkins doesn't like this, the many worlds theorists have risen up to repudiate it by saying, "We don't like the implications of that. Maybe there are multiple universes, each one of which is the actualization of a potential. And our particular universe is just one among these many." And so it's not the big "Wow!" that the Anthropic Principle advocates say it is.

I don't know how to evaluate that. Maybe if the Anthropic Principle argument continues to gain respect, we could say at best that it is a pointer. I don't think it's a proof for the existence of God. It's a pointer. But what is interesting is that it elicits some rather angry responses on the part of some who don't want it really to be a pointer to the divine. So, I'm not really giving you a constructive answer. I'm just describing again the kind of situation that you are alluding to.

h) Analogies and Lack of Data

Question: You said that you didn't think that analogy was scientific in character. It seems to me that there are numerous instances of use of analogy in scientific thought. Could you clarify your thinking on this?

Peters: The particular concern I have is with regard to sociobiology. The empirical work, at least in the case of E. O. Wilson,—as far as I know Dawkins does no empirical work, Wilson does—consists of gathering data on what happens in insect colonies and other animal populations with regard to reciprocal altruism and related matters. Then, arguing by analogy, they claim that this describes the human phenomenon.

It just seems to me that, with these human beings running around all over the place, one could do empirical experiments on human beings and find out whether or not the analogy is valid. The claim that the analogy is valid could then be subject to a falsification test.

So what I want to say initially is that this is not yet an empirical study of the human phenomenon. Conclusions are being drawn about the human phenomenon without actual empirical study. And so that's why I say, it's not scientific.

Maybe I'm overstating the case. Nevertheless, if I were an advocate of sociobiology I would kind of have nightmares wondering if someone would actually do an empirical experiment with human genes and disconfirm the theory.

At any rate, I just accept your point that analogy has been used in scientific thought. What I don't know, and maybe you do, is whether or not, analogy is sufficient for a scientist, once a theory is established. Would analogy then function at the level of hypothesis, and provide guidance for research program; or does the analogy simply count as knowledge?

Question [continued]: No, I don't agree with all the claims on analogy. My point was that some people have taken a strong positive position on the use of analogy, even to contend that analogy was some way a necessary condition in the formulation of scientific hypotheses. I am reminded particularly of *gedanken*[14] experiments as a good example of thinking using analogies.

Peters: Of course, analogies work. If I were at the beginning of the sociobiological project, I would say, "Gee, I wonder if human culture really is the selfish gene writ large." And I would say, "Hey, that's a good thing to go out and investigate." So if that is the role that analogy plays, I'll say that is just fine. But I wouldn't want to stop there and say that we've got knowledge. The role of the analogy should be to provoke a research program, and not be a conclusion. I don't see that happening.

Secondly, let me ask you this, does analogy likely play a bigger role when trying to theorize about phenomena we can't see than it would when it comes to phenomena that we can see? One thing about human culture is that you can see it. When it comes to subatomic physics you can't see it. There *gedanken* experiments are useful.

i) Salvation, Lifespan, and Repentance

Question: You have commented on science and the possibilities that it could provide our salvation. Science has doubled our lifespan, but there is no evidence that we have learned to repent any faster. At least we now have twice as long to do it.

Peters: Right, we can't even repent from smoking and obesity, let alone immorality.

j) Promethean Myth

Question [medical ethicist]: I think there have been three strains of thought on science through the 20th century. One was science as sanctification. Another would be that science is really not going to save us, and the Amish are an example of a people who pick and choose. And then there is science as evil. And there we find the Frankenstein myth and all of stories that have come from that, such as the Jeremy Rifkins of the world who view all of this progress as very negative. What do you think theology has to say about that third option, the evil part of it? Is there some way to prevent various Christian churches from supporting that idea?

Peters: That's an excellent question, because it really comes up in genetics and it could come up again in neuroscience. It's too early to tell about neuroscience.

It's actually the Promethean myth. Getting back to memes; if there is a meme in our culture, it's the myth of Prometheus, to be sure.

In the case of Frankenstein what you get is the discovery of electricity; and then the mad scientist crosses the line between life and death. That is where human beings ought not to go. That's the realm of the gods.

Actually it's the realm of nature. Nature in our modern world has replaced the gods of Olympus in ancient Greece. And the scientist is the Promethean character who could enter the realm of nature and then violate nature. And then nature is going to come back and get us. It's going to let loose the forces of chaos. And the monster of Frankenstein is just that, the monster of chaos out to kill its maker.

This is most vividly portrayed in *Jurassic Park*, which is the genetic version of Frankenstein. These dinosaurs, which are a nice scientific experiment, come back as the forces of chaos. There is deeply seated within Western culture this fear that the scientist is going to violate something of nature, and nature is going to come back and destroy us. The ecology movement gets its energy from the Promethean myth. Jeremy Rifkin, whom you mentioned, at the Foundation for Economic Trends, similarly capitalizes on this.

I'm frankly mad at the religious leaders who have fallen for this myth. And Jeremy Rifkin has organized groups of clergy—Christians, Jews, and in some cases Muslims and Buddhists—to rally against the progress of science, on the grounds that we are *playing God*, that we are violating nature, or something like that. I think that this is a dangerous myth, and we need to be critical, and not fall into that.

Do we want scientists to do stupid and dangerous things? Well, no we don't! Of course not! But does that mean that we should walk in trepidation about some violation of sacred reality that has this kind of chaotic threat to it? No, that is just not realistic. I think we need to be more realistic. So that is why I oppose saying science is "evil", and substitute the word "ambiguity"—that is, science could be pressed into the service of evil but, in itself, science is good.

Here's what I mean by ambiguity. On the one hand, science does absolutely marvelous things. Not only does it produce marvelous things, but it does something of value to the inner human psyche. We have a thirst for knowledge and a thirst for understanding. I think God put that there. And I think that the scientists do the whole society a favor by helping us to quench that thirst. On the other hand, scientists develop bombs. And there are sides to science over which we as society need to exert caution and regulation and all of those kinds of things. And in some ways science is like the other things in our lives. We have a moral responsibility to scientists like everything else.

So I don't believe that science has any kind of intrinsic evil to it in quite the way that the Frankenstein myth and the Promethean myth seem to say.

7. Sin

a) Murder and Chimpanzees

Question: Chimpanzees form groups and kill other groups of chimpanzees due to competition or for food. They have also found that chimpanzees will actually go to the other side of the mountain and kill other chimpanzees not for food, not for resources, just to do it. That eerily reminds me of what a lot of humans do.

Peters: I think what we enjoy about these animal studies is that we are really looking, among other things, for that which mimics human behavior. And we find some of these.

I grew up with pets. And I've had pets in my own family. Frankly, they sin. Not all the time. But there are clear cases in which they engaged in thievery, irritability, or sometimes downright meanness, and things like that. So what you and I call human sin might have continuity with the animal world. I just think it is observable that this is the case.

It is also true that when looking at higher primates you can find precedence for care, affection, and all of those kinds of things as well. That's the way it is with life in general. It's ambiguous. You can find things that are really blood red in tooth and claw, and you can find signs of tenderness and care as well. Which one of those anticipates God's kingdom? I think the latter probably does.

Question [continued]: How do we know murder is wrong when in nature you have the predator-prey relationship and constant killing? In animal social groups there are certain things you do and do not do for the success of the group. How do we as humans know that murder is wrong? Is this a result of social or behavioral evolution?

Peters: Lots of murders are committed within families. Right? In fact most of what we consider to be crimes of passion involve a family member murdering another family member probably against the ideas of sociobiology, expressed as the wishes of the DNA to replicate itself.

So, how does murder of one's brother or sister get explained?

Maybe we would say, "Killing a member of my family is wrong." What about killing an enemy outside the tribe? is that right? Perhaps a sociobiologist or evolutionary psychologist could explain the rise of this kind of morality as an expression of genetic kinship: killing people who are genetically distant is right because it contributes to the survival of my DNA, whereas killing someone with whom I share most of my DNA would be wrong. If this constituted our moral code regarding murder, then perhaps the sociobiologists could provide an adequate explanation by appeal to genetic proximity. This explanation fails, however, for two reasons. First, we can see how members of a family who share DNA kill each other. We give it a name: *fratricide*. Second, our Christian and modern moral codes proscribe murder of anybody, even persons with different DNA. The sociobiological explanation fails to account for either of these two phenomena.

Yet, we still need to account for the fact that Christians and modern Enlightenment people believe in universal human rights; and this belief in universal protection from murder leads to conflicting local moralities. We find this conflict in our own society today. On the one hand, we have a universal prohibition against committing murder, regardless of whether the victim is genetically close to us or distant. But, on the other hand, when we send our troops overseas to shoot enemies, we think it is justified. We justify killing foreigners not in the name of our own genetic survival but rather in the name of cultural abstractions such as freedom or justice or democracy or America's interests. The survival of our own DNA sequences does not motivate us to protect human life, even indirectly. If this is the case, what does?

Maybe God gave us a commandment: "thou shalt not kill." Might this count as an explanation?

b) Murder, Empathy and Suffering

Question: I think that one reason murder seems wrong to us is because we have developed the ability to empathize, to be able to see into somebody else's mind and experience their feelings, which I think is also unique to human beings.

Peters: I've wondered a lot about that. Is it possible that empathy precedes, in human experience, some of our moral codes? Because, you want to say, "Well, you shouldn't murder somebody else, because if you empathize with them and you look at murder from their point of view, you'll say, 'I don't want to die. I don't want that person to die.'" So when we have an in-group, which may or may not be genetically formed, we have empathy for everybody in the in-group. And then we don't for those who are in the out group.

So if you want to get us to behave morally towards those people who are the outsiders, you have to get us to empathize. And that's basically what social justice people do in our own society. They find a marginalized group of people and they find someone that suffered. Then they get the TV crew to show films of people being unjustly treated or suffering and not being attended to. Why do they do that? Well, because you and I watching those films say, "Oh, I feel empathy for those people who are suffering."

Just take the recent case of the U.S. soldiers in the Walter Reed Hospital. Reporters go in there with a camera and they see the soldiers with one leg missing being mistreated. Somehow or other the empathy says, "We don't want to be treated that way!" And so something happens. I guess the question phenomenologically would be, "Do you think empathy preceded some of these moral codes, and there is something built into the human psyche that wants to feel the feelings of others?" On the surface, this sounds like a good explanation: we each have a built-in genetic propensity for empathy, and this explains why cultures have moral proscriptions against inflicting suffering or murder on others.

I just want to say that's not true. It does not provide a persuasive explanation for me. I grew up in a neighborhood as a kid. From the earliest consciousness I had of being with my pre-kindergarten, friends there were some of us who had empathy and others who didn't. In my *Sin* book [*Sin: Radical Evil In Soul and Society*, 1994] I wrote about this observation. Louis and Bobby, for example, would catch crayfish, pull the legs off, and watch them suffer. I mean, they were four years old and doing this. They enjoyed watching other beings suffer. Why did they love watching suffering? I don't know; but this sadism was present at their beginnings.

Or maybe it's the case in the evolutionary development of the human race, some had empathy and others didn't. Those with empathy formulated the moral codes, and those without empathy had a hard time living up to them. I don't know.

c) Pollution and Guilt

Question: You mentioned theodicy and that original sin is coming back. I'm concerned and interested in the way it is coming back. Traditionally we had a fall and we could count on God to create everything perfect. Sin was ethical, not metaphysical. But sin seems to be coming back as a built-in result of the biological process. That would lead to a more metaphysical view of original sin. It's rooted in our nature. I don't want to throw out Christian orthodoxy, but I don't want to close my eyes to the way things are. Does this metaphysical view of original sin have the potential to cause a lot of dislocations in our theological system?

Peters: The bottom line is no, I don't think it causes dislocation. In fact, I am finding this whole discussion regarding what Christians want to say about redemption very enriching. You gave us two options: an ethical understanding of sin and a metaphysical. I'd like to come right in between those with a phenomenological understanding of sin, and see if a phenomenology of sin is on the way to drawing some theological conclusions. When you and I wake up and realize that we are set here in time and space and we are who we are and we've grown up in the families that we've grown up in and then we look around, and begin to become aware of the networks of sin and violence of which we are inextricably a part, and cannot extricate ourselves, it seems to me it's easy to see why Christian theologians have come up with a doctrine of original sin. We are born into it, and it is, as far as I can tell, observable. With regard to ethical sin, my mother worked very hard when I was young, to get me to look both ways before I crossed the street, and to get me to memorize the 10 Commandments, and get me to obey them. It was a lot of hard work that she had to do. Why? Well she had to shape this glob of hamburger into a meat ball, you know. And that's just kind of the way all mothers have to treat their little boys, and maybe the little girls too, as we come into the world. And so that's the way it is.

I think what is happening in these discussions of evolution, whether it's the selfish gene or related kinds of things, is that we are able to see a physical component, and not just a social component to what it is that we are born into. Even though I like to make jokes about that *Time* magazine article written from the point of evolutionary psychology, there is a way in which they are pointing to a reality which we just can't deny. We are born into a world of sin. Before we do anything that's moral or immoral, we are already in sin. And there is no way that we can extricate ourselves. So I'm finding this discussion of evolutionary biology and even sociobiology actually enriching in that regard. So before saying that it is metaphysical, I just want to say, hey, it's social and it's physical in character.

Question [continued]: Do you mean that it is just environmental, or is it also constitutional? Are we born with such a nature? And then I would also like to know if you are talking about just the pollution aspect of sin or also the guilt aspect of sin. I did my M. Div. at Westminster Seminary, a pretty conservative Reformed seminary, so original sin, both the guilt and the pollution of that, were things that were really hammered home.

Peters: Well, let's handle guilt first and then pollution with guilt. Do you feel guilty, you yourself, because of what the white slaveholders did to the slaves on the plantations in the deep South in the 1840s?

Question [continued]: No.

Peters: You don't? Why? Because you are not morally responsible?

Question [continued]: Correct.

Peters: Well, I feel guilty for that. How come I do and you don't?

Question [continued]: I've never thought about it before.

Peters: Do you feel guilty for anything that predates your birth?

Question [continued]: I guess theologically speaking I have always affirmed that I was guilty in the sense that I was born into sin, and born deserving of God's wrath. But, guilty for something that happened before I was born...

Peters: OK, I understand the words being born into sin and deserving God's wrath. But I am wondering, what it looks like when you flesh it out.

The kind of example that I think of is a sort of social contagion. Walter Rauschenbusch,[15] sort of the father of American liberal Protestantism, used the illustration of the dope peddlers on the corner selling heroin to the young kids. Well, you know, when those peddlers were young kids they were on the street corners and they got it. And so he had this doctrine of the social bequeathal of sin from one generation to another.

It seems to me that a lot of the networks of violence that you and I are born into were there before we came along, and there is no way that you can help it. My mother and father drank coffee around the breakfast table when I was a kid. I tasted it and didn't like it. But Juan Valdez down there, picking those coffee beans in South America is being exploited by international economic structures so that we can have inexpensive coffee on our tables. Is there any way to extricate yourself from that?

I want to ask, phenomenally, what does it mean to be born into original sin? That's the kind of thing that I am asking myself. I feel a certain level of guilt for participating in structures of injustice. Perhaps you don't. And if we go to court, and they ask, "Ted, are you responsible for exploiting Juan Valdez in Latin America?" Well, I'd be innocent, right? Because I never actually did anything. I'm just a very small cog in a very large system.

But I think there are aspects of human sin that are not the result of moral behavior. That's the nature of the phenomenon. And I think that the Christian understanding of original sin is able to account for guilt that is not the product of our own immoral behavior. By moral behavior I mean those acts where we sit there and choose between good and evil. Well I suppose that once in awhile we have a chance to choose between good and evil, but not often. I think most of the evil that we participate in really doesn't come to us as a choice. We just participate in it.

Pacifism would be an example. Pacifists kind of opt out of the system. But there is no way that we can, as taxpaying Americans for example, be without blood on our hands with regard to certain things that our government does. The blood is still polluting the pacifist's hands, despite the attempt to wash those hands clean by opting out of responsibility. So you might not feel direct guilt for, say, torture at Abu Ghraib; but I feel some guilt [as an American] even though I don't even know any of the victims or any of the perpetrators.

At any rate, I think that what happens in the discussion of evolution is that we are expanding, in a healthy way, our understanding of sin from being a bad moral action, to networks that perpetrate violence socially; then we move, finally, to the whole biological kingdom, of which we are a part. All of this belongs to God's creation. And when Christians use the word fall, it's all fallen. So all I'm doing now is trying to present a non-moral, non-ethical attempt to describe what we mean by inherited sin or original sin.

Question [continued]: To set your mind at ease, I want you to know that my wife and I have switched to fair trade coffee.

Peters: A little bit of guilt!

d) Genesis and Genetics

Question [seminary student]: My question has to do with the claim that we can provide a genetic explanation of sin. I believe that you are using the idea that we shouldn't lessen our view of sin to support this. We have it here even in science, so we can see that sin does exist.

I wonder how you would hold the scientific explanation of sin together with the Genesis explanation of sin. And if we have the Genesis explanation of sin, what do we do with an additional explanation that comes from science? How do we bring those together?

I would like to relate this to your first lecture's claim that Christian ethical doctrine is either true or false. In your first lecture you said either God called Abraham or God didn't; it's either true or false. How do you see that claim in relation to the Genesis narrative? Is there some middle ground?

Maybe you could use this example of a scientific explanation of sin versus the Genesis explanation of sin to clarify your understanding of the relationship between science and theology here.

Peters: This morning I distinguished between two ways of understanding genetic determinism. There is the sociobiological theory that says it's just the brute replication of DNA that is pressing evolution forward and determining what human culture is. Then there is another genetic approach, which is molecular biology. Molecular biology asks what specific genes do.

There was a longitudinal study a couple of years ago, on the question of abuse within families. Researchers studied boys who grew up in families in which they were treated abusively by their parents, predominantly by their fathers. Researchers watched them as they grew up, noting what the behavior patterns were like. And then when they grew up and became fathers, the study considered whether they abused their children according to the same model by which they were abused earlier. This was accompanied by DNA analysis.

The researchers found out that a portion of these children replicated their own childhood experience—that is, when they grew up, they abused their children in the same way their fathers had abused them. But a significant minority did not. Even though they were abused as children they grew up to be honest people who were responsible parents and held a good job and held high moral discipline for themselves. And the positive correlation, which was 100%, was a marker on the X-chromosome. There it was!

Now they didn't actually find a gene but they found a genetic marker. And so they surmise, there must be something in gene function that contributes to their ability to assess their own situation and make decisions to escape from the social determinism that they had as kids. Could moral strength be found in the genes? Looks like it.

On the other side there was a Dutch study a little bit earlier of a large family. There were 37 members in this family, and 17 of them were in and out of jail. The 17 were arrested for petty crimes, couldn't hold a job, they abused their children, and so on. And the other 20 were basically normal, productive citizens. And again there was a correlation. In this case it was a different marker, but also on the X-chromosome. And it looked like there is a strong genetic influence on a very identifiable pattern of behavior.

When I think about the Christian understanding of original sin, I ask whether we shouldn't have expected such findings to some degree. Are the scientists taking over the job of describing sin that has been vacated by the theologians? No, I don't see that at all. They are just doing specific studies of specific kinds of human behaviors. It is the theologian who needs to ask what the significance of these studies for understanding overall sinful behavior is.

So that's what I mean by saying that I think this aspect of the dialogue is actually enriching theology as we try to be realistic about what we understand to be the case, and what it is that we expect Christian ethics and Christian spirituality to accomplish in the face of these determinants.

e) Genesis, Evolution, and Empathy of God

Question: According to the Bible and Christian faith generally, the consequence of sin is death and corruption. This is not only of man's spirit and body, but the whole creation. Romans 8:20-22 says that the whole creation has been subjected to bondage through original sin. Now how do you reconcile your thoughts about God's using evolution with this teaching about original sin?

Humans have compassion and empathy for animals who are suffering. If God is more empathetic and compassionate than humans and if death and physical suffering of animals occurred prior to original sin, then why did God in his compassion and empathy not stop it?

Peters: Theologians need to have something to say about this when dealing with evolutionary theory. There are these passages in the Bible, such as from St. Paul, saying that "the wages of sin is death." There it looks like sin is the cause and death is the effect. And then in Genesis 2 and 3 you have paradise and then you have the fall and then death appears to begin after Adam and Eve are separated from the tree of life, not the tree of good and evil, but separated from the tree of life.

So the theologian needs to ask which comes first, sin or death? Getting back to phenomenology, I really think there is a circle at work in human consciousness regarding sin and death. In some ways murder is the ultimate sin; and fear of being murdered or fear of death—actually, fear of non-being—gives rise to anxiety. Anxiety, in turn, leads to sinful behavior. Paul Tillich and some other neo-orthodox theologians point to fear of death or anxiety as the ground for our striking out with violence against others. Reinhold Niebuhr said that anxiety is the fertile ground within which sin grows. Once you begin to look at human phenomena through those eyes, to me it makes an enormous amount of sense to see how death and anxiety over death give rise to sinful actions. Phenomenologically, death comes first with sin as a byproduct.

According to the Darwinian model of evolution, death entered the world long before humans began sinning. But even if you go back behind human sinfulness, Charles Darwin himself was bothered by the predator-prey relationship and the gratuitous violence that seemed to pervade all of nature in the struggle for life. We humans inherit this struggle from our biological predecessors. The theologian has to ask what role does that play? Is our state of sin something we have inherited from our evolutionary past?

In the Genesis story it looks like the reverse order: sin happened first and death happened second. But, upon closer look, Adam and Eve are eating fruit before they are expelled from the Garden of Eden. Well, what about the fruit trees? And what about the other plants that are dying in the process to fertilize the fruit trees? So, the line between life and death is not absolute. The human and all of nature, the plants as well as the animals, belong together.

I always find it interesting that as Adam and Eve are being expelled from the garden, and the angel with the fiery sword is placed at the gate so they can't get back in—and remember that Adam and Eve were without clothes, they couldn't make it to Nordstrom's before leaving the garden—so God provides them with what? Leather aprons. Well where did God get the leather? What animal had to die for God to get that leather? So you are not likely to go to the Adam and Eve story to justify vegetarianism. Well, I don't think the intention of that story is to give us a sequence of cause and effect.

[Parenthetically, scientific creationists insist that God's original creation of the world was good, and this means that all animals including dinosaurs were originally vegetarians. After Adam and Eve introduced sin into the world, animals along with humans began to eat meat. For us to eat meat, some living creature must die. Creationists emphasize that sin led to death. Theistic evolutionists, in contrast to the creationists, do not feel obligated to keep this ordering. I call this the "temporal sequence conflict" between creationism and theistic evolution.]

Let me say something about the role that Genesis 1 to 5 particularly plays in my thinking, more specifically, Genesis 1:1-2:4a, which is the seven-day creation account. I don't see these as accounts of a set of events that happened once upon a time in our chronological past. I see them rather as symbolic descriptions of the whole story of God's relationship to the creation.

I like to think of you and me as living now within the story of Genesis 1:1-2:4a somewhere. We are somewhere between Genesis 1:1, when God opens his mouth to say, "Let there be a creation," and Genesis 2:4a, where God says, "And behold, it's all very good." And I don't think we are going to get 2:4a until we get to the New Jerusalem and the Apocalypse. You'd use the term fallen only if there was a paradise that predated us. But what if paradise postdates us? That is where we are going. Then maybe the word fall isn't the best.

We are sort of on the way to being created and dubbed very good. That's about the best way I can put these scriptural commitments, which I take very seriously, together with evolutionary theory, which looks like it has a different understanding of temporal sequence and how things develop. Be that as it may, you and I find ourselves right now really is in a struggle for existence that Darwin's theory describes pretty well.

Question [continued]: That doesn't yet address the implication of evolutionary theory would have for God's character and compassion.

Peters: Oh, that's right, you did ask that. What I want to say about God's character would be drawn from "behold, it is very good" in the Genesis passage, and then jumping to Revelation 21, there will be healing and no more crying or pain. I want to say, those biblical symbols tell us about God's character. And if the Christian claim about God's being gracious is right, I think that's what we are going to see. We only see it fragmentarily right now.

How can the evolutionary treatment of animals' suffering, physical sufferings, be reconciled with God's character of love, compassion, mercy. If a human being were raising animals, and had a large plot of wooded land into which he just released them all and allowed them to fight for survival, with results come as they may and hope for the best, we can predict that the strong animals would kill and devour the weak ones. Knowing this, we would consider such a person very cruel to the weaker animals. And that would, in a sense, be what God would be doing using evolution to create animals and man. All I can say is I share your question. I think you're asking the right question, and the best I can do is point to directions where we might look for the answers. Yes, it does make God look kind of cruel. And it gave Charles Darwin some bad days when he actually thought about it. It gives me bad days when I think about it, too.

f) Embarrassment, Shame and Guilt

Question: We talked a lot about sin. How do you relate sin to the emotions of embarrassment, shame and guilt?

Peters: Well, I haven't really thought a lot about that. So I don't have a quick answer. I do think they are distinguishable but interrelated. Tell us why you raise the question. Maybe you have some wisdom in there to share with us.

Question [continued]: I don't have any wisdom about it because I know very little about sin.

Peters: But you know about embarrassment, shame and guilt.

Question [continued]: Nevertheless, it just seems to me that in common day parlance these are the terms that we use. I don't think we use the term sin. But I think there is a relationship that I just don't understand. I am asking the question because I don't know the answer.

Peters: If I think over the next couple of hours and come up with an answer I'll find you.

g) Genetic Heritage and Jesus

Question: I'm interested in getting your response to the phenomenon of Jesus in understanding sin, the relation of sin to genetics, and human behavior in terms of being born into a society that has very undesirable behaviors, violence and thievery, and things like that. Here comes Jesus born with our genetic heritage, into the same kind of society we are, and yet there is a completely different quality to his life. And we look to him as a different way than that which is so common among us. What does that have to say about some of these issues? Does that put constraints on some of the things that are being said about the relation between genes and sin?

Peters: Those theologians who like sociobiology will ask the kind of question you are asking, and then ask, "Does Jesus really represent an evolutionary advance?" Why? Because he takes kin altruism and he expands it, so that now we can care for the interests of people who do not belong in our genetically privileged group.

I observe the same thing about Jesus even though I am not sure I want to give a sociobiological explanation for it. I think Jesus in the Sermon on the Mount is radical when he says love your enemy. And if I am sitting there listening to Jesus in the Sermon on the Mount, who is my enemy? Well, people outside the tribe, and in some cases almost literally outside the tribe. Those people who are outside my group, which in that case could be racial as well as social and political. And Jesus said, "you know, this is the way that God does things. God loves the other. And I want you to be perfect as God is perfect."

I think that Jesus is giving no quarter to genetic preference. That is my interpretation. He didn't say it that way, but if the selfish gene is operative, Jesus is saying, "don't obey the genes. Disobey them. And if you are perfect as God is, you are going to love somebody who is genetically distant rather than somebody who is close."

You could, if you are within the parameters of sociobiology, say, well that's an evolutionary advance. Let me just say, I am sympathetic to that. But I don't really belong to that particular school because, even though I think that Christian theology needs to make sense out of evolution, I don't think the evolutionary scheme should trump the Christian theological scheme. I don't want to, somehow or other, get permission from the evolutionists to do my Christian theology. Even though there might be something to the relevance of evolution for understanding Christian commitments.

The other thing we notice is that despite Jesus' radical teaching about *agape* love, nobody obeys it, as far as I know. I don't think anybody did in Jesus' time, and they don't right down to the present day. And so Jesus' command to love the other as you love yourself, or to be perfect as God is perfect, sits out there as a moral demand that nobody lives up to or virtually nobody lives up to. So there we are. There is a difference between God's perfection and what we human beings actually do.

Jesus was special, you say. Quite frequently we will say that Jesus was sinless, even if we might also say Jesus knew sin. What I think as a systematic theologian, and this may be just too artificial, is that we could claim that Jesus did not commit sin in the moral sense. The moral sense of sin would be the choice between good and evil when we choose the evil side. I'll bet you that Jesus did not do that. But I don't think that Jesus was without sin completely. He knew sin in the sense that he was born into a network of violence in which all kinds of bad things happen, and over which he had no control. In fact his very destiny precipitated all kinds of reactive violence. If St. Paul says Jesus knew sin, it was not in the sense that he sat around like a systematic theologian and said, "Oh, I understand sin." Jesus knew sin in the sense that he was involved in the network that we think of as sinful. I think that fits.

h) Salvation and Condemnation

Question: I have two questions that are separate but related. First, was there any necessity for Jesus to be born of a woman in order to affect salvation for mankind? The second is related to a claim you make in your book *God—the World's Future*. You claim that there will be universal salvation. How then do you understand Jesus' statement in Matthew 25:46, "And these will go away into everlasting punishment, but the righteous into to eternal life," which apparently contrasts two eternal states?

Peters: Let me say in regard to the first question about Jesus being born of a woman, I have never really thought about that. One of the important aspects of God's presence in Jesus, I think, is that Jesus is like us in many respects. He even had a job. He was a carpenter for a while. So I would say that there is nothing special about being born of a woman. In fact, being born of a woman and being ordinary is the whole point. So, maybe I am not tuned to the significance of your question. But that is my first answer.

The second one is really a toughie. The question that people just need to wrestle with is this: if we think of salvation in terms of resurrection to everlasting life, is it for everybody? Or do we divide the human race into two groups: those who get saved and those who are subject to everlasting damnation?

Well, the first thing you do is go back and take a look at the Bible. There are a lot of passages just like the one that you cited going back to the book of Daniel where there is this double destiny. There is one for those that are faithful and just. They get their everlasting reward. And there is another for those who are apostate and depart from the ways of God. They get everlasting damnation. And you can find it even in the words of Jesus, as you have mentioned there. So we could list eight or ten Bible passages like this. But you can also list some other ones, such as when St. Paul says repeatedly, "In Adam all die, and in Christ *all* are made alive."

And so there you sit, with Scripture and Scripture. And what is a theologian to do? Well, as I argue somewhat carefully in that book [*God—The World's Future*] that this is a genuine difficulty, an honest difficulty. So, where does a theologian want to tip? I mean, you could have the teeter-totter just sort of sit out there. But if you want the teeter-totter to tip, what I do is say, let's see what the implications would be if God is gracious. If St. Paul says, "While we were yet sinners, Christ died for us," he is appealing to a God of grace. So it's the grace of God for those of us in our state of sin that is so important to the gospel. I claim that, even if you and I are sinful, there's a sense in which God's grace is still at work. So that leads me down the road to say, "Maybe, if the teeter totter has to tip, it's going to be on the side of universal salvation."

Now, here's another thought, and you probably saw it in the book. Imagine that you are renewed and formed by the Holy Spirit. And that like God you are motivated by love. You are motivated by empathy, and you are motivated by compassion. You now have the heart of God. And suppose you go to heaven. You are up there in heaven, and you decide to take a walk. You walk over and find there is a rail. You look over this rail. On the other side you see hell. What's happening there is that other souls are suffering torment. And if you have the heart of God, your compassion is going to stir you up. You will not be able to sleep at night in heaven, because the image of torment exacted on the damned will give you night mares. You'll have no inner peace. So, I wonder if it could be heaven for godly people if they know that somebody else is suffering.

So what are these comments I'm making? These are finite, theological speculations. Are they dogmas? No, they are not. They are just an attempt to work through some difficulties in how to make the Bible make sense on this kind of question. And so I firmly respect those people who tip the teeter totter to the other side, to the side of double destiny. After all, they have the words of Jesus on their side, right? But, on the other hand, I am thinking, maybe God's grace will win out. So what do you think?

Question [continued]: Regarding God as love and being able to enjoy heaven, knowing others are suffering, there's the story that Jesus related about the rich man and Lazarus. When he died Lazarus went to Abraham's bosom, and the rich man was taken to torment. Apparently then, assuming it is a literal account, which I believe it is, Abraham and Lazarus were able to enjoy the comfort of their environment, while being able to be in communication with those who were suffering. So to me that says that once we die and are given better, greater, or perfect knowledge, the suffering of those who have chosen their state, I guess, will not even enter our minds in heaven. Or we will know that it is just, and we will not be bothered by it in some way. That's how I reconcile it.

Peters: Let me say that what you are saying is coherent, it is understandable. No matter which side of the teeter totter tips, the other side is going to have some problems.

But let me ask you about Lazarus and the rich man. In this life, Lazarus is suffering. He is poor. He can't help himself. He is diseased. The dogs lick his sores. It is really humiliating for Lazarus. And the rich man walks past him every day and pays no attention. Lazarus dies. Isn't it great that Lazarus goes to the bosom of Abraham, and in a sense he gets the dignity and the comfort in heaven that he didn't get on earth? Well, what is Jesus' point? His point is this: "all of you here on earth, who walk past somebody who is suffering and pay no attention, I want you to listen to me." I mean that really is the whole story within which the story of Lazarus and the rich man is placed, isn't it?

So I don't think it is about life in heaven. I think it is about your and my responsibility for loving those people who are suffering around us. And Jesus is using the story in order to make this point. Actually, it is kind of an ethical point. What do you think about that?

Question [continued]: I think it is both, because in my understanding all parables of Jesus were based on either things that were actually happening or could happen.

Peters: I probably would not grant that assumption. I think Jesus made up these stories on the spot. That doesn't mean that they are trivial. I'm just saying that I think he made the stories up in order to make a point to the people to whom he was speaking at the moment.

Question [continued]: Yes, but part of what I said was that any story, if he did make it up, would have been something that could have happened.

Peters: I'll accept that.

8. Sociobiology

a) Conflict within the Genotype

Question: According to Dawkins, violence becomes easier or almost mandatory in terms of insuring the replication of one's own genotype. Similar to the story of one twin killing her twin sister, we had a real situation here in Goshen in which a young adult woman conspired with her boyfriend to murder her mother.

I haven't seen Dawkins' actual proposal, but I think if he were being careful about it he would want to propose this as a probabilistic law, not as an absolute law. The probabilities would distribute the fewest incidents closest to home and the most instances of violence much farther from home.

Our empathy resources are also easily exhausted when dealing with catastrophes far from home. The genocide in Darfur is barely on the radar screen. Tens of thousands dying in war in the Congo, that is no longer on the radar screen.

Can you speak more at length about genetics and in-groups?

Peters: What you are surmising regarding Dawkins' defense against my talking about one twin murdering another, is pretty much what he would do, I think. The sociobiologist would respond exactly that way. "Well, Ted, we are not talking about individual cases. We're talking about statistics, and what happens over the long haul."

There actually have been some disciples of sociobiology that have done some empirical studies. For example, one that they like to show considers child abuse in families where a parent, usually the father, violently abuses the child. Statistically, if it is a stepfather, there is more likely to be violence than if it is a biological father. Ergo, the selfish gene theory is exonerated or confirmed by this. Well, I would say that this is relevant data; whether it is sufficient I don't know, but I do understand that.

On the other hand I want to ask if one twin murders another, where does the theory really count? When it comes to our understanding of murder, is it any accident that the first murder in the Bible is one brother killing another brother? I think we know in human experience that the threat of violence within families is really very high. It can happen almost any time. We always think it is tragic, and all of that, but it has been with us since the dawn of the human race. It would seem to me that if the selfish gene theory were capable of making a prediction, you would see a drastic statistical difference between the genetically determined in-group and the out-group, where the out-group membership would suffer the most murders. But, this is not the case. The majority of crimes of passion occur within genetic in-groups. This should count as disconfirmation of the selfish gene theory, shouldn't it?

In addition to statistical probability, I just want to say that I think anecdotal evidence and cultural insight is at least relevant. What I think is an observable phenomenon is that the human race divides into in-groups and out-groups. And the in-groups protect one another, and they have lower empathy for those who are in the out-group. So your description of the fate of people over there in Africa, who are suffering, is relevant. Even though we know they are human beings, we go back to our basic daily agendas without helping them. Yes, that is exactly what happens. Now the question is: does the selfish gene theory explain this? I don't think so. It is the phenomenon, but I am not sure that the selfish gene explains it.

Here's why. One great big in-group is America. And America has out-groups, those that we go to war against. And then when you line up a hundred American soldiers do they look genetically proximate? I don't think so! There are all different kinds of races of people in this particular in-group. And I have a hunch that, if peoples around the world continue to migrate and communicate, the lines between the in-group and the out-group would constantly be redrawn, but not according togenetic criteria.

I think of the phenomenon of gangs. I served as a pastor on the south side of Chicago for a little while, and did some youth work. I had a chance to get to know some of the kids in the gangs. And, boy, there is a strong in-group *esprit de corps* in those gangs. There is the establishment of territory and the commitment of violence against the outsiders. Gang membership was not determined by genetic proximity. In retrospect, I can't see anything genetic about that at all.

There is no doubt that social division is a human phenomenon. But I am not sure the selfish gene would explain why it is that you are a member of one gang and not of another. Well, of course, if you are a member of the Vietnamese group, yes, OK. But not every gang is racially organized. Rather than race, turf or geography plays a more important role in determining membership in the in-group. So what I want to say is that this phenomenon of in-group and out-group requires theological and ethical attention, to be sure. But I haven't seen where the selfish gene theory actually helps in the explanation at this point.

b) Race and Gang Wars

Question: What about the issue of genotype and phenotype? I mean race is often something you can identify empirically.

Peters: There is no question that human history is replete with race wars. But the reason I brought up my experience in the south side of Chicago is that quite frequently it is not race that distinguishes one gang from another, the Black Keystone Nation say, from the Kenwood Disciples. All the members of both gangs were of the same race. But there is a line between the two groups. The line was 63rd Street. So that's why I am saying that I am not sure genetics can help us understand why these two groups are angry at each other.

Question [continued]: I agree with you. I am just trying to strengthen the case. The genotype difference between people of two different races is incredibly small. The phenotype could be very different in terms of skin color or some other observable feature. The point is that if the selfish gene explanation is going to work, it has to work at the level of the genotype. And yet it seems that even in the case of racial violence, you are choosing whom to kill based on the phenotype. Besides how would your genotype detect someone else's genotype and know which one to knock off?

Peters: How would Dawkins respond to that? I am not sure. Maybe the theory would really work in an ancient, pre-industrial society, where you could tell groups of people apart by their genotypes. Today, in our pluralistic society, like I say, the lines are drawn and they are not phenotypically distinctive.

c) Gang Wars and Cultural Damage

Question [medical ethicist]: Ted, I think we can explain the gang warfare as an aptitude. I have an opposable thumb. I can do things with it that help me in evolutionary terms. I can also do things that harm me. Gang warfare is a tendency among humans and primates to form in- and out-groups, and then destroy the out-groups. That doesn't mean that every time that aptitude is used it is going to be used in a way that helps us. It is just that this aptitude is genetically determined as a tendency, sociobiologically, and in that way I think we could explain a lot of this.

You could continue it a little farther by looking at cultural evolution as well. If our goal is not just to propagate our genes but to propagate our cultural values, then again we will form whatever in-group/out-group lines we can in order to propagate both our culture and our genes.

Peters: If I understood you, I guess I want to ask whether dogs wag tails or tails wag dogs. As you know, I don't believe in cultural evolution. I don't believe in memes.

I think that what happened was that Dawkins formulated this rather coherent theory of the selfish gene in biology; and then he extrapolated the whole thing and pinned it on culture. And I'm not sure that it is a template that fits. Culture changes, but that doesn't mean it evolves. I don't see any mechanism in culture that looks remotely like natural selection in biology. So that's why I tend to just plain not believe it.

I think in this case, we have human behavior of the type that you are talking about. Why is it that we draw lines? Why is it that we use weapons? And why is it that we try to further our group's interests over against competing groups? I mean that is a phenomenon, and it needs an explanation. And I think the scientific question would be whether or not the selfish gene really provides us with an illuminating explanation. I just think it falls too far short to do that.

So I don't want to start the other way around and say, oh, we have this great theory about genetic influence or genetic determinism, and now we want to…I think that is the tail waging the dog.

[By the way, I offer my own alternative to sociobiology in my book, *Sin: Radical Evil in Soul and Society*. I begin with the anxiety theory of the neo-orthodox theologians Tillich and Niebuhr; and I find it explains in-group vs. out-group behavior quite exhaustively.]

d) Selfish Gene, Wilderness and Yawning

Question [biology student]: I have studied the selfish gene theory only once. It seems this applies well to wildlife. I think it is a pretty darn good theory biologically. But the problem is, when you take a biological theory apply it to humanity, you are in a totally different realm.

The behavior of animals living in the wilderness is almost exclusively genetic. The environmental influence is there, but it is small. But with humanity environment plays a huge role in how our behavior develops. I can think of only one purely genetic human behavior, and that is yawning. And we have things like culture, we have morality, we have religion. So I think that is actually a downfall of the sociobiological selfish gene theory.

Peters: So the only thing that we do that is completely genetic is yawn? I've got a question for you. I've done a lot of traveling. I've been on every continent with the exception of Antarctica. And everywhere I go that I see human beings, I see them picking their noses. And to me this is one of the chief arguments against the Intelligent Design theory, because if God had designed our noses, he could have done a slightly better job. Does that fit into genetic determinism?

Question [continued]: I'll have to ask my professor about that one.

9. Trinity

a) Basic Concept

Question: In my experience an awful lot of Christians do not understand the Trinity the way you talk about it. They seem to have a Tri-theist theology in which Jesus, the Holy Spirit, and God are all separate. Each has a separate job to do. So I do not recognize the Trinitarian theology you have presented residing in churches today.

Peters: Well, I'm aware of that. There's really been a renaissance in Trinitarian theology starting after the Second World War. It began with Karl Rahner in the Roman Catholic tradition and Karl Barth in the Protestant tradition. And my summary of Rahner is basically a summary of that. It's really not about the number three at all.

What I usually hear in churches, and I got this when I was a kid in catechism, is that the mystery of the Trinity is how three can be one and one can be three. And I wanted to pull my hair out. Hans Küng tells the story of a Bavarian priest on Trinity Sunday. He gets up in the pulpit, and he says, "The Trinity is a mystery, and because it is a mystery, I've got nothing to say about it." And then he left the pulpit, and they had no sermon.

It's not about the number three. I think it's really about God's involvement with the world. And this is what the Trinitarian renaissance is about. It's a story about how God the Creator of the world, through the incarnation and the drama which is the life, death and resurrection of Jesus Christ and your and my continuing consciousness of that, wrought by the Holy Spirit, is internal to the three persons of the Trinity operating within the world. That's what it's about.

I just find this a new and exciting retrieval of things that really had been there all along in the Christian tradition but became kind of ossified over the years into the thinking of three in one and one and three. So when I talk with Muslims, I really want to deal with how God can be fully involved with the nitty-gritty of daily life in a way that the incarnation or the doctrine of the Holy Spirit indicates. To me, that's really the issue. Muslims are a little bit more sympathetic to that, because for them God is involved, even though they are trying to protect God's transcendence and oneness.

Let me just say that I would like to see the conversation in the future go that direction.

b) Jesus' Relation to the Father

Question: I think the verse John 17:22 sheds some light on Jesus' relationship to the Father in the Trinity. Jesus is praying to the Father and says, "And the glory which you gave me I have given them, that they may be one just as we are one." They are not identical, but maintain personality and individuality. This implies that Jesus and the Father are separate, but united like a husband and wife.

Peters: I think that at minimum the oneness of the divine in this case is complex in character. Just as the oneness that we would find in the church would be complex, as you were suggesting. Each one of us is an individual. And so the oneness of Jesus with the father is a complex oneness. It's still a oneness. But they are not identical.

c) Rational Mind

Question: You said that the Trinity and the personal relationship that the Christian has with the divine are two distinctive aspects of Christianity. To what part of the human being is that personal relationship addressed?

Peters: You want me to help you out on what does it mean to have a personal relationship with the divine? Is that the heart of your question?

Question [continued]: Consider this from the perspective of the scientist, which you claim is agnostic. I am wondering how, in this context, you understand the meaning of a personal relationship. This does not address my rational mind. What in me is addressed?

Peters: With regard to the atmosphere or culture that surrounds science, since the 18th century especially, but even back in the 17th century, what we mean by a rational disposition is to be impersonal. Basically you are disinterested in the experiments that you are running, and disinterested in the body of knowledge that is being developed. This led to the belief that being dispassionate, removing one's passions from the body of knowledge, is what counts as science. And right down to the present day that's what people believe, even though practicing scientists all know that the scientists themselves are quite passionate people. But, if possible, the discipline ought to be thought of as impersonal, dispassionate, disinterested, and objective, although we don't use the word objective much anymore.

So we have a subculture that surrounds science that is supposedly rational. This was also the case in the 18th century when America was being founded and France went through those serious revolutions. It was thought then that the problem in society was religion. In particular the problem was Catholicism and Protestantism.

I want to say that a personal relationship would include the rational mind. But it's not reducible to the rational mind. The Word of God speaks to our heart. When our heart has heard God speak, then the heart enlists the mind to help understand rationally what to make of God's Word. In the words of Raimon Panikkar, God's Word speaks to the question of what is meaningful in our lives.

I also think that when God speaks both to our heart and to our reason, it pulls us upward towards what is the good. And that movement towards what is the good becomes definitive of who we are in a meaningful way.

Francis Collins used the dimension of prayer. When we talk to God in prayer, we are talking about the deepest, most personal things that are who we are. I myself get a lot of benefit out of thinking that the Bible provides the symbols of my faith. And over a period of time, living my life meaningfully out of these biblical symbols, is a form of confirmation that the God who transcends them all is co-present with me. Let me just say, that is the way it works for me. I don't know how else to think about it.

Notes

1. Carl Reiner, an American actor, film director, producer, writer, and comedian.
2. NOMA: Non-Overlapping Magisteria of science and religion.
3. J. Robert Oppenheimer, the scientific director of Los Alamos during WW II, had become influenced by Niels Bohr's vision for international control of nuclear weapons, but was entangled in the immediate realities of war.
4. Paul Charles William Davies (1946 -) is a British-born physicist and writer.
5. Star Wars was the common name for the Strategic Defense Initiative (SDI). It was proposed by U.S. President Ronald Reagan on March 23, 1983. The system proposed was to use ground and space based systems to defend the United States from attack by ballistic missiles from, primarily the Soviet Union. This was to be a new initiative replacing the doctrine of mutually assured detruction (MAD). SDI was never employed. Failure was on the basis of fundamental physics. But it was also opposed by some on the basis of policy.
6. This was once an actual bag factory in Goshen. It has since been converted to house shops, a pottery studio, and a cafe.
7. *On the Origin of Species by Means of Natural Selection.*
8. Christian de Duve, Nobel Prize in Physiology or Medicine, 1974.
9. *Can You Believe in God and Evolution?: A Guide for the Perplexed*, by Ted Peters and Martinez Hewlett
10. Benjamin Breckinridge Warfield (1851–1921) was the Principal of Princeton Seminary from 1887 – 1921.
11. Antje Jackelén (1955-) is Bishop of Lund, Sweden, former Director of the Zygon Center for Religion and Science in Chicago, and the 2003 speaker at the Goshen Conference on Religion and Science.
12. Philip Hefner, Professor emeritus of systematic theology (Lutheran School of Theology at Chicago), former Director of the Zygon Center for Religion and Science in Chicago, and the 2006 speaker at the Goshen Conference on Religion and Science.
13. *The Anthopic Cosmological Principle* (Oxford Paperbacks, 1986) John D. Barrow, Frank J. Tipler, John A. Wheeler.
14. The term *gedanken Experiment* is German for "thought experiment". A thought experiment is not fanciful. It must be possible to actually arrange the elements considered in a real laboratory and each proposed measurement must be one that can be performed in a real laboratory, even though it may be technically difficult. *Gedanken Experimenten* have been critical in the development of the quantum theory and were the cornerstone of Einstein's 1905 paper on special relativity.
15. Walter Rauschenbusch, is known as the Father of the Social Gospel movement of the early 20th Century. He believed that Christian principles must be translated into actions that promote compassion, justice, and social change.

Index

C

D

I

J

K

L

M

N

O

P

S

T

U

V

W

Y

About Pandora Press

Pandora Press is a small, independently owned press dedicated to making available modestly priced books that deal with Anabaptist, Mennonite, and Believers Church topics, both historical and theological. We welcome comments from our readers.

Visit our full-service online Bookstore:
www.pandorapress.com

Laureen Harder, *We Bear the Loss Together: A History of the Mennonite Aid Union* (Kitchener: Pandora Press, 2008). Softcover, 107 pages. ISBN 978-1-894710-86-2

Jacob J. Rempel, edited by David J. Rempel Smucker, *Consider the Threshing Stone*, translated by David J. Rempel Smucker and Eleanore (Rempel) Woollard (Kitchener: Pandora Press, 2008). Softcover, 179 pages. ISBN 978-1-894710-83-1

Ruth Derksen Siemens, *Remember Us: Letters from Stalin's Gulag (1930-37). Volume One: The Regehr Family* (Kitchener: Pandora Press, 2008). Softcover, 399 pages. ISBN 978-1-894710-82-4

Fernando Enns, *The Peace Church and the Ecumenical Community: Ecclesiology and the Ethics of Nonviolence* (Kitchener: Pandora Press, 2007). Softcover, 360 pages. ISBN 978-1-894710-78-7 ISSN 1480-7432

Peter C. Erb , ed., *Martyrdom in an Ecumenical Perspective: A Mennonite-Catholic Conversation* (Kitchener: Pandora Press, 2007). Softcover, 200 pages. ISBN978-1-894710-81-7 ISSN 1711-9480

Neal Blough, *Christ in our Midst: Incarnation, Church and Discipleship in the theology of Pilgram Marpeck* (Kitchener: Pandora Press, 2007). Softcover, 275 pages. ISBN 978-1-894710-77-0

James Urry, *None but Saints* (Kitchener: Pandora Press, 2007). Softcover, 370 pages. ISBN 1-894710-71-8

Jeremy M. Bergen, Paul Doerksen, and Karl Koop, eds., *Creed and Conscience: Essays in Honour of A. James Reimer* (Kitchener: Pandora Press, 2007). Softcover, 301 pages. ISBN 978-1-894710-80-0

Werner O. Packull, *Peter Riedemann: Shaper of the Hutterite Tradition* (Kitchener: Pandora Press, 2007). Softcover, 252 pages. ISBN 978-894710-76-3

H.G. Mannhardt, *The Danzig Mennonite Church: Its Origins and History from 1569-1919*, translated by Victor G. Doerksen (Kitchener: Pandora Press, 2007). Softcover, 286 pages.
ISBN 978-1-889239-04-0

R. Martens, M. Jantzen and H. Neufeldt, *Windows to a Village: Life Studies of Yarrow Pineers* (Kitchener, Pandora Press, 2007). Softcover, 444 pages. ISBN 978-1894710-79-4

Peter Riedemann, *Love is like Fire: The Confession of an Anabaptist Prisoner* (Kitchener: Pandora Press, 2006) Softcover, 84 pages. ISBN 1-894710-72-X

Gerke van Hiele with Marion Bruggen, Ina ter Kuile and Frans Misset, *Encountering the Eternal One: A Guide for Mennonite Churches* (Kitchener: Pandora Press, 2006) Softcover, 120 pages.
ISBN 1-894710-75-4

Andreas Ehrenpreis and Claus Felbinger, *Brotherly Community: The Highest Command of Love* (Kitchener: Pandora Press, 2006) Softcover, 146 pages. ISBN 1-894710-74-6

Jakob Hutter, *Brotherly Faithfulness: Epistles from a Time of Persecution* (Kitchener: Pandora Press, 2006) Softcover, 250 pages. ISBN 1-894710-73-8

Robert John Russell, *Cosmology, Evolution, and Resurrection Hope* (Kitchener: Pandora Press, 2006) Softcover, 118 pages.
ISBN 1-894710-67-3

Nathan E. Yoder and Carol A. Scheppard, eds., *Exiles in the Empire: Believers Church Perspectives on Politics* (Kitchener: Pandora Press, 2006) Softcover, 266 pages. Scriptural and topical indexes. ISBN 1-894710-68-1

Helmut Isaak, *Menno Simons and the New Jerusalem* (Kitchener: Pandora Press, 2006) Softcover, 158 pages. Bibliography. ISBN 1-894710-69-X

Leah Dawn Bueckert and Daniel Schipani, eds. *Spiritual Caregiving in the Hospital. Windows to Chaplaincy Ministry* (Kitchener: Pandora Press, 2006) Softcover, 230 pages. ISBN 1-894710-65-7

Lawrence M. Yoder, *The Muria Story. A History of the Chinese Mennonite Churches in Indonesia* (Kitchener: Pandora Press, 2006). Softcover, 386 pages. ISBN 1-894710-60-6

Ralph Lebold, *Strange and Wonderful Paths. The Memoirs of Ralph Lebold.* (Kitchener: Pandora Press, 2006). Softcover, 236 pages. Bibliography and index. ISBN 1-894710-66-5

Karl Koop, ed. *Confessions of Faith in the Anabaptist Tradition, 1527-1660* (Kitchener: Pandora Press, 2006). Softcover, 366 pages. Scripture index. ISBN 1-894710-62-2

Alle Hoekema and Hanspeter Jecker, eds. *Testing Faith and Tradition. A Global Mennonite History: Europe* (Kitchener: Pandora Press, 2006; co-published with Good Books). Softcover, 324 pages. Indexes. ISBN 1-56148-550-0

John A. Lapp and C. Arnold Snyder, gen.eds., *Anabaptist Songs in African Hearts. A Global Mennonite History: Africa* (Kitchener: Pandora Press, 2006; co-published with Good Books) Softcover, 292 pages. Indexes. ISBN 1-56148-549-7

Harry Loewen, *Between Worlds. Reflections of a Soviet-born Canadian Mennonite* (Kitchener: Pandora Press, 2006). Softcover, 358 pages. Bibliography. ISBN 1-894710-63-0

H. H. Drake Williams III, ed., *Caspar Schwenckfeld. Eight Writings on Christian Beliefs* (Kitchener: Pandora Press, 2006). Softcover, 200 pages. Index. ISBN 1-894710-64-9

Maureen Epp and Carol Ann Weaver, eds., *Sound in the Land: Essays on Mennonites and Music* (Kitchener: Pandora Press, 2006). Softcover, 220 pages. Bibliography. ISBN 1-894710-59-2

Geoffrey Dipple, *"Just as in the Time of the Apostles": Uses of History in the Radical Reformation* (Kitchener: Pandora Press, 2005). Softcover, 324 pages. Bibliography and index. ISBN 1-894710-58-4.

Harry Huebner, *Echoes of the Word: Theological Ethics as Rhetorical Practice* Anabaptist and Mennonite Studies Series (Kitchener: Pandora Press, 2005). Softcover, 274 pages. Bibliography and index. ISBN 1-894710-56-8 ISSN 1494-4081

John F. Haught, *Purpose, Evolution and the Mystery of Life,* Proceedings of the Fourth Annual Goshen Conference on Religion and Science, ed. Carl S. Helrich (Kitchener" Pandora Press, 2005). Softcover, 130 pages. Index. ISBN 1-894710-55-X

Gerald W. Schlabach, gen. ed., *Called Together to be Peacemakers: Report of the International Dialogue between the Catholic Church and Mennonite World Conference 1998-2003* (Kitchener: Pandora Press, 2005). Softcover, 77 pages. ISBN 1-894710-57-6 ISSN 1711-9480

Rodney James Sawatsky, *History and Ideology: American Mennonite Identity Definition through History* (Kitchener: Pandora Press, 2005). Softcover, 216 pages. Bibliography and index. ISBN 1-894710-53-3 ISSN 1494-4081

Harvey Neufeldt, Ruth Derksen Siemens and Robert Martens, eds., *First Nations and First Settlers in the Fraser Valley (1890-1960)* (Kitchener: Pandora Press, 2005). Softcover, 287 pages. Bibliography and index. ISBN 1-894710-54-1

David Waltner-Toews, *The Complete Tante Tina: Mennonite Blues and Recipes* (Kitchener: Pandora Press, 2004) Softcover, 129 pages. ISBN 1-894710-52-5

John Howard Yoder, *Anabaptism and Reformation in Switzerland: An Historical and Theological Analysis of the Dialogues Between Anabaptists and Reformers* (Kitchener: Pandora Press, 2004) Softcover, 509 pages. Bibliography and indexes. ISBN 1-894710-44-4 ISSN 1494-4081

Antje Jackelén, *The Dialogue Between Religion and Science: Challenges and Future Directions* (Kitchener: Pandora Press, 2004) Softcover, 143 pages. Index. ISBN 1-894710-45-2

Ivan J. Kauffman, ed., *Just Policing: Mennonite-Catholic Theological Colloquium 2001-2002* (Kitchener: Pandora Press, 2004). Softcover, 127 pages. ISBN 1-894710-48-7.

Gerald W. Schlabach, ed., *On Baptism: Mennonite-Catholic Theological Colloquium 2001-2002* (Kitchener: Pandora Press, 2004). Softcover, 147 pages. ISBN 1-894710-47-9 ISSN 1711-9480.

Harvey L. Dyck, John R. Staples and John B. Toews, comp., trans. and ed. *Nestor Makhno and the Eichenfeld Massacre:* (Kitchener: Pandora Press, 2004). Softcover, 115pages. ISBN 1-894710-46-0.

Jean Janzen, *Elements of Faithful Writing* (Kitchener, Pandora Press, 2004). Softcover, 49 pages. ISBN 1-889239-03-8

Jeffrey Wayne Taylor, *The Formation of the Primitive Baptist Movement* (Kitchener: Pandora Press, 2004). Softcover, 225 pages. Bibliography and index. ISBN 1-894710-42-8 ISSN 1480-7432.

James C. Juhnke and Carol M. Hunter, *The Missing Peace: The Search for Nonviolent Alternatives in United States History,* 2nd ed. (Kitchener: Pandora Press, 2004) Softcover, 339 pp. Index. ISBN 1-894710-46-3

Louise Hawkley and James C. Juhnke, eds., *Nonviolent America: History through the Eyes of Peace* (North Newton: Bethel College, 2004, co-published with Pandora Press) Softcover, 269 pages. Index. ISBN 1-889239-02-X

Karl Koop, *Anabaptist-Mennonite Confessions of Faith: the Development of a Tradition* (Kitchener: Pandora Press, 2004) Softcover, 178 pages. Index. ISBN 1-894710-32-0

Lucille Marr, *The Transforming Power of a Century: Mennonite Central Committee and its Evolution in Ontario* (Kitchener: Pandora Press, 2003). Softcover, 390 pages. Bibliography and index, ISBN 1-894710-41-x

Erica Janzen, *Six Sugar Beets, Five Bitter Years* (Kitchener: Pandora Press, 2003). Softcover, 186 pages. ISBN 1-894710-37-1

T. D. Regehr, *Faith Life and Witness in the Northwest, 1903–2003: Centennial History of the Northwest Mennonite Conference* (Kitchener: Pandora Press, 2003). Softcover, 524 pages. Index, ISBN 1-894710-39-8

George F. R. Ellis, *A Universe of Ethics Morality and Hope: Proceedings from the Second Annual Goshen Conference on Religion and Science* (Kitchener: Pandora Press, 2003) Softcover, 148 pages.
ISBN 1-894710-36-3

Donald Martin, *Old Order Mennonites of Ontario: Gelassenheit, Discipleship, Brotherhood* (Kitchener: Pandora Press, 2003). Softcover, 381 pages. Index. ISBN 1-894710-33-9

Mary A. Schiedel, *Pioneers in Ministry: Women Pastors in Ontario Mennonite Churches, 1973-2003* (Kitchener: Pandora Press, 2003) Softcover, 204 pages. ISBN 1-894710-35-5

Harry Loewen, ed., *Shepherds, Servants and Prophets* (Kitchener: Pandora Press, 2003) Softcover, 446 pages. ISBN 1-894710-35-5

Robert A. Riall, trans., Galen A. Peters, ed., *The Earliest Hymns of the* Ausbund: *Some Beautiful Christian Songs Composed and Sung in the Prison at Passau, Published 1564* (Kitchener: Pandora Press, 2003) Softcover, 468 pages. Bibliography and index. ISBN 1-894710-34-7

John A. Harder, *From Kleefeld With Love* (Kitchener: Pandora Press, 2003) Softcover, 198 pages. ISBN 1-894710-28-2

John F. Peters, *The Plain People: A Glimpse at Life Among the Old Order Mennonites of Ontario* (Kitchener: Pandora Press, 2003) Softcover, 54 pages. ISBN 1-894710-26-6

Robert S. Kreider, *My Early Years: An Autobiography* (Kitchener: Pandora Press, 2002) Softcover, 600 pages. Index ISBN 1-894710-23-1

Helen Martens, *Hutterite Songs* (Kitchener: Pandora Press, 2002) Softcover, xxii, 328 pages. ISBN 1-894710-24-X

C. Arnold Snyder and Galen A. Peters, eds., *Reading the Anabaptist Bible: Reflections for Every Day of the Year* (Kitchener: Pandora Press, 2002) Softcover, 415 pages. ISBN 1-894710-25-8

C. Arnold Snyder, ed., *Commoners and Community: Essays in Honour of Werner O. Packull* (Kitchener: Pandora Press, 2002) Softcover, 324 pages. ISBN 1-894710-27-4

James O. Lehman, *Mennonite Tent Revivals: Howard Hammer and Myron Augsburger, 1952-1962* (Kitchener: Pandora Press, 2002) Softcover, xxiv, 318 pages. ISBN 1-894710-22-3

Lawrence Klippenstein and Jacob Dick, *Mennonite Alternative Service in Russia* (Kitchener: Pandora Press, 2002) Softcover, viii, 163 pages. ISBN 1-894710-21-5

Nancey Murphy, *Religion and Science* (Kitchener: Pandora Press, 2002) Softcover, 126 pages. ISBN 1-894710-20-7

Biblical Concordance of the Swiss Brethren, 1540. Trans. Gilbert Fast and Galen Peters; bib. intro. Joe Springer; ed. C. Arnold Snyder (Kitchener: Pandora Press, 2001) Softcover, lv, 227pages. ISBN 1-894710-16-9

Orland Gingerich, *The Amish of Canada* (Kitchener: Pandora Press, 2001) Softcover, 244 pages. Index. ISBN 1-894710-19-3

M. Darrol Bryant, *Religion in a New Key* (Kitchener: Pandora Press, 2001) Softcover, 136 pages. Bib. refs. ISBN 1-894710- 18-5

Trans. Walter Klaassen, Frank Friesen, Werner O. Packull, ed. C. Arnold Snyder, *Sources of South German/Austrian Anabaptism* (Kitchener: Pandora Press, 2001; co-published with Herald Press.) Softcover, 430 pages. Indexes. ISBN 1-894710-15-0

Pedro A. Sandín Fremaint y Pablo A. Jimémez, *Palabras Duras: Homilías* (Kitchener: Pandora Press, 2001). Softcover, 121 pages. ISBN 1-894710-17-7

Ruth Elizabeth Mooney, *Manual Para Crear Materiales de Educación Cristiana* (Kitchener: Pandora Press, 2001). Softcover, 206 pages. ISBN 1-894710-12-6

Esther and Malcolm Wenger, poetry by Ann Wenger, *Healing the Wounds* (Kitchener: Pandora Press, 2001). Softcover, 210 pages. ISBN 1-894710-09-6.

Otto H. Selles and Geraldine Selles-Ysselstein, *New Songs* (Kitchener: Pandora Press, 2001). Poetry and relief prints, 90 pages. ISBN 1-894719-14-2

Pedro A. Sandín Fremaint, *Cuentos y Encuentros: Hacia una Educación Transformadora* (Kitchener: Pandora Press, 2001). Softcover 163 pages. ISBN 1-894710-08-8.

A. James Reimer, *Mennonites and Classical Theology: Dogmatic Foundations for Christian Ethics* (Kitchener: Pandora Press, 2001) Softcover, 650 pages. ISBN 0-9685543-7-7

Walter Klaassen, *Anabaptism: Neither Catholic nor Protestant*, 3rd ed (Kitchener: Pandora Press, 2001) Softcover, 122 pages. ISBN 1-894710-01-0

Dale Schrag & James Juhnke, eds., *Anabaptist Visions for the new Millennium: A search for identity* (Kitchener: Pandora Press, 2000) Softcover, 242 pages. ISBN 1-894710-00-2

Harry Loewen, ed., *Road to Freedom: Mennonites Escape the Land of Suffering* (Kitchener: Pandora Press, 2000) Hardcover, large format, 302pages. ISBN 0-9685543-5-0

Alan Kreider and Stuart Murray, eds., *Coming Home: Stories of Anabaptists in Britain and Ireland* (Kitchener: Pandora Press, 2000) Softcover, 220pages. ISBN 0-9685543-6-9

Edna Schroeder Thiessen and Angela Showalter, *A Life Displaced: A Mennonite Woman's Flight from War-Torn Poland* (Kitchener: Pandora Press, 2000) Softcover, xii, 218 pages. ISBN 0-9685543-2-6

Stuart Murray, *Biblical Interpretation in the Anabaptist Tradition*, Studies in the Believers Tradition (Kitchener: Pandora Press, 2000) Softcover, 310pages. ISBN 0-9685543-3-4 ISSN 1480-7432.

Loren L. Johns, ed. *Apocalypticism and Millennialism* (Kitchener: Pandora Press, 2000) Softcover, 419 pages. Indexes. ISBN 0-9683462-9-4 ISSN 1480-7432

Later Writings by Pilgram Marpeck and his Circle. Volume 1. Trans. Walter Klaassen, Werner Packull, and John Rempel (Kitchener: Pandora Press, 1999) Softcover, 157 pages. ISBN 0-9683462-6-X

John Driver, *Radical Faith. An Alternative History of the Christian Church,* ed. Carrie Snyder. Kitchener: Pandora Press, 1999) Softcover, 334 pages. ISBN 0-9683462-8-6

C. Arnold Snyder, *From Anabaptist Seed.* (Kitchener: Pandora Press, 1999) Softcover, 53 pages. ISBN 0-9685543-0-X
Also available in Spanish translation: *De Semilla Anabautista,* from Pandora Press only.

John D. Thiesen, *Mennonite and Nazi? Attitudes Among Mennonite Colonists in Latin America, 1933-1945* (Kitchener: Pandora Press, 1999) Softcover, 330 pages. Bibliography, index. ISBN 0-9683462-5-1

Lifting the Veil, ed. Leonard Friesen; trans. Walter Klaassen (Kitchener: Pandora Press, 1998). Softcover, 128 pages. ISBN 0-9683462-1-9

Leonard Gross, *The Golden Years of the Hutterites,* rev. ed. (Kitchener: Pandora Press, 1998). Softcover, 280 pages. Index. ISBN 0-9683462-3-5

William H. Brackney, ed., *The Believers Church: A Voluntary Church,* (Kitchener: Pandora Press, 1998). Softcover, viii, 237 pages. Index. ISBN 0-9683462-0-0 ISSN 1480-7432

An Annotated Hutterite Bibliography, compiled by Maria H. Krisztinkovich, ed. by Peter C. Erb (Kitchener: Pandora Press, 1998). (Ca. 2,700 entries) 312 pages. Softcover, electronic, or both. ISBN (paper) 0-9698762-8-9/(disk) 0-9698762-9-7

Jacobus ten Doornkaat Koolman, *Dirk Philips. Friend and Colleague of Menno Simons,* trans. W. E. Keeney, ed. C. A. Snyder (Kitchener: Pandora Press, 1998). Softcover, xviii, 236 pages. Index. ISBN: 0-9698762-3-8

Sarah Dyck, ed./tr., *The Silence Echoes: Memoirs of Trauma & Tears* (Kitchener: Pandora Press, 1997). Softcover, xii, 236 pages. ISBN: 0-9698762-7-0

Wes Harrison, *Andreas Ehrenpreis and Hutterite Faith and Practice* (Kitchener: Pandora Press, 1997). Softcover, xxiv, 274 pages. Index. ISBN 0-9698762-6-2

C. Arnold Snyder, *Anabaptist History and Theology: Revised Student Edition* (Kitchener: Pandora Press, 1997). Softcover, xiv, 466 pages. Index, bibliography. ISBN 0-9698762-5-4

Nancey Murphy, *Reconciling Theology and Science: A Radical Reformation Perspective* (Kitchener, Ont.: Pandora Press, 1997). Softcover, x, 103 pages. Index. ISBN 0-9698762-4-6

The Limits of Perfection: A Conversation with J. Lawrence Burkholder 2nd ed., with a new epilogue by J. Lawrence Burkholder, Rodney Sawatsky and Scott Holland, eds. (Kitchener: Pandora Press, 1996). Softcover, x, 154 pages. ISBN 0-9698762-2-X

C. Arnold Snyder, *Anabaptist History and Theology: An Introduction* (Kitchener: Pandora Press, 1995). Softcover, x, 434 pages. Index,bibliography. ISBN 0-9698762-0-3

Pandora Press
33 Kent Avenue Kitchener, ON N2G 3R2
Tel.: (519) 578-2381 / Fax: (519) 578-1826
E-mail: info@pandorapress.com
Web site: www.pandorapress.com